PRAISE FOR
ENLIGHTEN UP!

I have just read the final lines of Beth Gibbs's book *Enlighten Up!*
Like the finish of any worthwhile journey, I am both enriched and
sad to see it end. The author's sharp and clever sense of humor, her
real-life revelations, and her fascinating perspectives bring to life
the 5-layered "kosha" model from the yoga tradition as a map to
better living that would otherwise seem inaccessible and strange.
Whether you are new to yoga-based lifestyle "medicine" or a long-
time practitioner, through Beth's perceptive eyes and words, you
will be engaged, entertained and, dare I say it, enlightened up! I'm
already looking forward to diving back in for a second go around
and putting all the practical tools for a more satisfying life into daily
use. Won't you join me on the adventure?

— **Baxter Bell, MD**
co-author of *Yoga for Healthy Aging*

Ms. Gibbs seeks to help the reader understand oneself as opposed
to fixing oneself. She has clearly spelled out the layers of awareness
and shares her journey to enlightenment through her many stories.
This book is enriched with yoga exercises that a beginner like myself
was able to appreciate.

— **Marilyn Martin, MD**
The Resource Group

Love, peace and happiness are not external goals; they dwell within us. *Enlighten Up!* shines light on the koshas, or five layers of self-awareness, to arouse self-inquiry and observation of the multiple levels of being beyond blood, bone and tissue. Gibbs's essays on each of the five layers are expressed in down-to-earth and honest language, written from her personal and professional perspective and experience as a yoga therapist, teacher and long-time practitioner. She has seen and digested much along her journey and generously shares her insights. Yoga philosophy and Sanskrit terminology can be difficult to explain. However, the stories in *Enlighten Up!* demystify the metaphysical interplay between body, mind and spirit that impact the choices we make in life and inform how we feel about ourselves and others. When we understand the energies of the koshas, we possess the keys to self-mastery to fulfill our greatest potential and cultivate inner peace. This book is an invitation to "know thyself." Best of all, *Enlighten Up!* has stories for everyone regardless of age or ability. It can be enjoyed by the yoga neophyte, seasoned practitioner, and the skilled teacher. It is a valuable tool for living yoga off the mat.

— **Jana Long**
Executive Director, Black Yoga Teachers Alliance

Enlighten Up! is a book of hard-earned wisdom that will make a difference in your life. It's already made a difference in mine, especially the chapter called "Bitchcraft," which not only outlines Gibbs's evolution in turning fear and anger into assertiveness but outlines protocols, self-inquiry and practices for us to do the same. In fact, every chapter has guidance for us to rise through those layers of self-awareness. Don't be fooled by the title into thinking this is just another spiritual book. As a Black woman just past a tormented menopause, Gibbs's story is her own, yet she uses it to shine light on our own blind spots. *Enlighten Up!* is deeply and profoundly spiritual and oh so human, written with compassion and ever-expanding self-awareness. As you read, you are nodding, saying "yes" to the truth of being a woman in a "complicated world." As you read, you say "yes" to the author as a guide through the deepest wisdom of yoga as a lived experience. As you read, you are saying "yes" to Beth Gibbs, because she feels like your new best friend. *Enlighten Up!* will be one of those books I will turn to again and again for inspiration.

— **Amy Weintraub**
Founder, LifeForce Yoga Healing Institute and
author of *Temple Dancer*

I can't imagine a better person to take us on a journey through the koshas. Beth Gibbs has fifty years of yoga practice under her belt plus hard-won wisdom from life lived in the real world. Add in her teaching experience, her easy-to-understand and accessible writing style, and her awesome sense of humor and what you get is an entertaining read that provides you with deep understanding of how you can use the koshas to better make sense of your everyday life in the modern world and to navigate through its inevitable ups and downs with greater ease and contentment.

— **Nina Zolotow**
Editor-in-Chief, Yoga for Healthy Aging blog and
co-author of *Yoga for Healthy Aging*

Unabashedly frank, Beth Gibbs shares personal stories with humor and intimacy. Weaving together wisdom she gleaned from experience, concrete practices she engaged to transform her life, and knowledge of the yogic kosha model, the author delivers a book of counsel and direction that supports wholeness and integration.

— **Deborah Adele**
author of *The Yamas & Niyamas*

In *Enlighten Up!*, Beth Gibbs manages to condense years of practice and teaching into a book that can uplift yoga practitioners and teachers alike. She uses humor, storytelling, science and yoga wisdom to enlighten us and help us navigate our lives using the ancient tools of yoga.

— **Jivana Heyman**
Director, Accessible Yoga and
author of *Accessible Yoga*

ENLIGHTEN UP!

ENLIGHTEN UP!

FINDING CLARITY CONTENTMENT AND RESILIENCE IN A COMPLICATED WORLD

BY BETH GIBBS

EMERALD LAKE
BOOKS
Sherman, Connecticut

Enlighten Up!
Finding Clarity, Contentment and Resilience in a Complicated World

Copyright © 2020 Beth Gibbs

Cover design © 2020 by Mark Gerber

Song lyrics from *Show Up & Be Heard* by Wah! (Wah! Music), copyright 2002. Used by permission of Wah Devi.

Connection to stuff personal story used by permission of Nina Zolotow.

Spiritual grace personal story used by permission of Sandy Eimers.

Spiritual grace personal story used by permission of Maria Mendola Shamas.

Books published by Emerald Lake Books may be ordered through your favorite booksellers or by visiting emeraldlakebooks.com.

Library of Congress Cataloging-in-Publication Data

Names: Gibbs, Beth, author.
Title: Enlighten up! : finding clarity, contentment and resilience in a
    complicated world / Beth Gibbs.
Description: Sherman : Emerald Lake Books, 2021. | Summary: "Want to find
    more clarity, contentment and resilience in this complicated world we
    all live in? Cultivating self-awareness on a practical everyday
    down-to-earth level is the first step. When we lack self-awareness, it
    gets in the way of navigating life's ups and downs. Enlighten Up!
    presents a contemporary view of self-awareness based on a 3,000-year-old
    model that provides a broader foundation for self-exploration than the
    more well-known mind/body model. Explore this five-layer model for
    self-awareness through stories, tips and simple yoga practices to learn
    how to apply them to your own life"-- Provided by publisher.
Identifiers: LCCN 2020040142 (print) | LCCN 2020040143 (ebook) | ISBN
    9781945847349 (paperback) | ISBN 9781945847356 (epub)
Subjects: LCSH: Self-consciousness (Awareness) | Self-help techniques.
Classification: LCC BF311 .G473 2021 (print) | LCC BF311 (ebook) | DDC
    158.1--dc23
LC record available at https://lccn.loc.gov/2020040142
LC ebook record available at https://lccn.loc.gov/2020040143

This book is dedicated to Joseph Le Page.

CONTENTS

FOREWORD

Beth Gibbs's book *Enlighten Up!* provides profound insights into the different layers of our being: physical, energetic, psycho-emotional, intuitive and spiritual. These layers, or *koshas,* are part of an ancient philosophy called "Vedanta," which Beth has presented in an easily accessible way for modern readers. Each of us faces the challenge of how to integrate, accept and then unfold all the different facets of our lives. This was a topic that the ancient *rishis,* or seers, sought to explain. Beth explains the topic from her own experience by means of a series of personal essays.

The purpose of this journey through the different layers of our being is to find balance, contentment and resilience in everyday life, which is often challenging. More than an author, Beth is a living example of finding this balance. In her long career as an educator, counselor, yoga teacher and yoga therapist, she has developed the ability to see the positive in every situation and challenge. It is this ability to find a way to take life positively that makes Beth's book so real and practical in our daily lives.

The beauty of the book is that it takes us layer by layer through the levels of our being, starting with the physical body. She details how the health of the body begins with acceptance, authenticity and finding those areas where we naturally feel good about ourselves.

She then goes into diet and lifestyle showing us that digestion has two phases—both what we eat and what eats us. Sometimes, dealing with a physical problem simply requires greater attention and acceptance. We also see the distinction between having things just to have them and having those things that can actually support the health and substance of the body.

At the second level, the level of breath and energy, Beth shows us that the body is more than a physical machine. It requires breath and energy, and this energy and vitality comes from the way we think and feel. She uses her own experience of chronic back and hip pain to show how shifts in energy can also create shifts in the body, explaining that the process of cultivating energy is one of enlightening: becoming lighter, living with greater ease, opening our senses to the world around us, and becoming part of everything.

At the third layer, which deals with the mind, thoughts and emotions, Beth explains how to understand the connection between thoughts and emotions and how to be able to observe them as they are happening. By becoming aware of them within the body—noticing the shades of anger, fear, happiness and sadness we experience—we come to see where and how they live and to recognize that we can actually work with them constructively. Beth also explores some of the ways people defeat themselves in an endless struggle of negativity and complaining and shows us instead how to develop a SASSY bill of rights: Strength, Authenticity, Skill, Serenity and remaining Young-at-heart.

At the fourth level, Beth outlines the importance of "the witness," which when awakened allows us to see our lives, including our problems, challenges and layers of conditioning, with greater clarity. Beth explores how to awaken the witness with body, mind and breathing techniques, and how to cultivate conscious choice in our lives rather than being victims of our conditioning. In this section, we learn to explore our own shadows and to see how their voices can actually free us from darkness and suffering.

In the fifth layer, the level of bliss, Beth shows how we can make the best of life in any situation, opening to experiences that unfold our potential, positive qualities and possibilities. We also see that whatever is truly valuable is already present and waiting within our own being. Through the tools and techniques presented in this book, we find that bliss and contentment can be found in the simplest joys of everyday living and those joys can show up in surprising and unexpected ways.

In *Enlighten Up!*, Beth Gibbs shows how this five-layer method can lead to clarity, contentment and internal resilience in all facets of daily living.

—Joseph Le Page
founder of Integrative Yoga Therapy

PREFACE

*Life is like a game of cards. The hand
that is dealt you represents determinism;
the way you play is your own will.*

— Jawaharlal Nehru

Becoming self-aware is how you learn to play your game of cards. It's the foundation needed to build a balanced life and find clarity, contentment and resilience in a complicated world.

As a yoga teacher and a keen observer of life, I've witnessed in others and personally experienced how a lack of self-awareness gets in the way of navigating life's ups and downs. Many personal growth books on this topic offer advice, rules and programs focused on the mind/body connection since thoughts, feelings, beliefs and attitudes can positively or negatively affect biological functioning and behavior. What they often do not include are three additional layers of self-awareness: energy, intuition and spirituality.

Enlighten Up! is the first book to present a contemporary view of self-awareness based on a 3,000-year-old model from the Upanishads, an East Indian wisdom tradition. The five layers of self-awareness provide a broader foundation for self-exploration than the more well-known Western mind/body model.

The bookshelves in dorms, apartments and homes I have lived in as well as the condo I live in now have held stacks of self-help and personal growth books. The ones I benefited from most were those in which the author shared how they used their tips, techniques, programs or advice to help them with their life issues. So it's not surprising that when I found myself writing this book, I did it by sharing my experiences, stories and reflections along with those of colleagues, friends and students.

This book is written with honesty, authenticity and humor. Humor is important because it can take the edge off of tension, stress and difficult situations. My sense of humor is a bit ironic, satirical and offbeat. For example, I once saw a mug in a card shop that declared, "Life's a bitch and then you die." I laughed loud and long because life often feels like a bitch and the last part is true for us all. However, if we manage to face life with a healthy dose of self-awareness, we can enlighten up and heal. And in case you are thinking I am someone who has got it all together, let me assure you—I do not. I'm a recovering co-dependent and introverted perfectionist who is a work in progress.

I have been happy, sad, joyful, pissed off, ready to fight and scared to death. Thankfully, I have never been in a war, physically or sexually attacked (harassed, yes—what woman hasn't been, #MeToo). I have not been bankrupt, poor or homeless. If I had any of those experiences, I believe the ability to enlighten up would have helped me manage the stress, seek help, and find useful ways to navigate through the worst of it.

So sit down, put your feet up, grab a cup of tea (or a glass of wine), relax, read, think, laugh and enjoy.

INTRODUCTION

The path of understanding follows
an ascending spiral rather than
a straight line.

— Joanna Field

What Is Self-Awareness?

Self-awareness is the ability to see, understand and accept our beliefs, habits and behavior without judgment. Then we can consciously choose to make changes, remain unchanged with full awareness of the consequences, or find acceptance and peace of mind if change is not possible. Cultivating self-awareness is a life-long journey that can be started at any age.

Self-awareness is a state, not a trait. We don't find and keep our self-awareness. It will ebb and flow, shift and change depending on our situation and state of mind. Science now recognizes that our thoughts, feelings, beliefs, attitudes and how we handle stress can positively or negatively affect our mental and physical health.

Modern research on the psychological aspects of self-awareness can be traced back to 1972 when psychologists Shelley Duval and Robert Wicklund developed their theory of self-awareness.

When attention is directed inward and the individual's consciousness is focused on himself, he is the object of his own consciousness—hence "objective" self-awareness.[1]

However, this concept is not new. For centuries, philosophers have pondered the connection between self-awareness and health. The first known mention of the five layers of self-awareness (the *koshas*) comes from the Taittiriya Upanishad, a 3,000-year-old philosophical text from India.[2]

The Upanishads were written in India during a time when people began to shift the focus of religious life from external rites and sacrifices to internal spiritual quests. Each of the thirteen texts share stories, ideas, instructions and insights into the meaning of consciousness and self-awareness that are as relevant today as they were 3,000 years ago.

The five-layer model offers an ideal framework for the theory and practice of self-awareness. The model proposes that we are much more than a mind interacting with a body. Understanding ourselves through the five layers of being provides a 360-degree view of what it means to be human and gives us a broad foundation for self-exploration. Along with that foundation comes a wide variety of practices to foster self-awareness.

The five layers are:

1. **Physical** (*annamaya kosha*) – This includes your body and your environment. This is you: your size, shape, gender

---

1   T. S. Duval and R. A. Wicklund. *A Theory of Objective Self Awareness.* January 1, 1972, Oxford Press.

2   *The Upanishads.* Translated by Eknath Easwaran. Nilgiri Press, June 1, 2009.

identification, race, ethnicity, anatomy, physiology, your home and the planet we all share.

2. **Energetic** (*pranamaya kosha*) – This includes your breath and energy levels. The oxygen you breathe nourishes your body and brain and sustains life. Your energy is the invisible *life force* that animates you at all levels and enables you to think, create, move, love, work and navigate all that life brings.

3. **Mental** (*manomaya kosha*) – Your thoughts, beliefs and emotions. This is how you think, what you think about, what you believe, and how you experience and express your emotions.

4. **Intuitive wisdom** (*vijnanamaya kosha*) – This is the witness, the ability to observe all of your layers and your life with compassion and without judgment to consciously make (or not) more informed choices.

5. **Bliss** (*anandamaya kosha*) – This is your connection to something larger than yourself. This can be spiritual, religious or a deep connection to a healthy passion or the natural world.

How Do We Become Self-Aware?

IN ADDITION TO VIEWING THE FIVE layers as important aspects of ourselves, we can also view them as a framework for developing self-awareness in all aspects of our lives. Taking the Nine Steps to Self-Awareness is one way to do that. The nine steps are:

1. Become aware of your body and environment.
2. Become aware of your breath and energy states.
3. Identify your thoughts and feelings.
4. Explore your beliefs.
5. Turn the mind back on itself.
6. Take skillful action.

7. Find your bliss.

8. Connect to your bliss.

9. Bring bliss into your daily life.

The sections that follow in this book describe the five layers and present the recommended steps to take in relation to that layer. The chapters in each section then offer specific practices to work with these steps.

I have adapted The Nine Steps to Self-Awareness from the original Ten Steps to Freedom[3] for simplicity and practicality.

Why Is Self-Awareness Important?

NO MATTER YOUR SIZE, SHAPE, COLOR, condition or position in life, when you were born, your five layers came into this world with you. They are accessible to you twenty-four hours a day, every day of the year.

Each layer operates moment to moment in our daily lives. If we move through our lives on autopilot with no awareness of our body, how we're breathing, or our habits, routines, beliefs, emotions, impulses and reactions, we lose power. When we succeed in understanding how our layers work and how they are connected, we will gain a better understanding of how and why we react the way we do to what life presents. Then the choices we make are conscious. Our responses are healthier, balanced and more productive. This requires attention and effort. It will take time, but the result will be more clarity, contentment and resilience.

The process of paying attention is often influenced by the past; how we think about it, how often we misremember it, and how it affects our feelings about ourselves in the present. It's important

---

3   "Ten Steps to Freedom," student handout by Joseph Le Page. Integrative Yoga Therapy, 1998.

to understand that the road to self-awareness is not a sprint; it's a lifelong marathon requiring intention, skill and practice. Developing self-awareness can help you:

- find better solutions for your problems.
- make better lifestyle choices.
- manage stress.[4]
- enhance relationships that can be improved.
- end toxic relationships that cannot be improved.
- reduce worry, fear and anger.
- lessen the tendency to judge yourself and others.
- understand what you can and cannot control.
- learn how to relax.

Research shows that people with self-awareness skills tend to have better psychological health, a positive outlook on life, and are likely to be more compassionate to themselves and others. This larger sense of self results in the ability to navigate life from a calm center no matter the swirls, whirls and storms that will inevitably surround us.

Most of us choose to begin this journey with the body and the environment because they are readily observable through our five senses. Although body and environment may be the first focus, it's important to know that all five layers are inseparable, interrelated and will be affected as well.

Having a mental picture of the five layers is a helpful tool. Some writers describe them as a set of Russian dolls, with one layer nesting inside the other. Others use the analogy of an onion, presenting the

---

4   The American Psychological Association says most Americans suffer from moderate to high stress, with 44 percent reporting an increase in stress levels over the past five years (apa.org/helpcenter/stress.aspx), and a 2013 *JAMA Internal Medicine* paper states that 70 to 90 percent of primary care doctor visits are attributed to stress.

journey to self-awareness as peeling away the layers one by one. The traditional depiction is of five concentric circles.

In the yoga wisdom tradition, each circle represents a layer of being, beginning with bliss as the largest outermost circle and devolving inward from intuitive wisdom to mental and then energetic, with the physical as a small circle in the center.

It's at that center where we move through our life in Earth School. It's where we experience all that makes us happy, excited, upbeat and feeling good—the ups. Here, we also find ourselves dealing with all that leaves us feeling scared, empty, sad and suffering—the downs. If we stay on autopilot, we go around and around the rim of our small circle, experiencing the ups and downs of our life over and over with no awareness of what we can do to either make things better, keep them as-is with an awareness of the consequences, or find peace of mind if no change is possible.

Autopilot dissolves as we evolve beyond the rim of our small circle. As we go, we begin to recognize our layers as a unified whole, even though we work with them separately. We can view the ups and downs of our life with awareness. The ups are still wonderful, but now we know they are temporary. The downs are still painful, but now we know they too are temporary. We acknowledge what we experience and respond with a greater measure of clarity, contentment and resilience to whatever life brings our way.

Clarity means seeing things as they are and not how we want them to be. When we bring clarity to our life, we will have a better understanding of our thoughts, beliefs, habits and behavior patterns. Clarity is a wonderful side effect of self-awareness that allows us to see ourselves and our everyday reality as it is, not hidden behind a veil of wishful thinking or denial.

Contentment is a state of sustained calm that permeates all five layers of self-awareness no matter what happens in our life. It is different than happiness. Happiness comes in waves and is temporary. It's similar to excitement. Both depend on external sources to keep those feelings of arousal, elation and exhilaration going. Contentment does not depend on externals, like finding your soul mate, landing a dream job, or finding that perfect little black dress that makes you look ten pounds thinner. Contentment is a state of accepting what is. It's a quiet, deep sense of acceptance, calm and gratitude.

Resilience is the ability to rebound quickly from a crisis, tragedy, trauma or a serious case of "stress mess." Highly resilient people won't fall apart easily, and when we do ('cause we will), it won't be for long. Resilient people:

- know how to handle their emotions.
- keep calm in stressful situations.
- are empathetic.
- cultivate self-awareness.
- practice acceptance.
- engage in self-care.

This book will help you build your self-awareness skills and find clarity, contentment and resilience in our complicated world.

How to Use this Book:
A Suggestion

THIS BOOK IS DIVIDED INTO FIVE sections, one for each layer of self-awareness. Following a description of each layer, narrative chapters trace the self-awareness process through personal stories and examples of familiar experiences, like marriage, parenting, divorce, death, widowhood, living single, racism, sexism, rejection, emotional funks, family relationships (both functional and dys-functional), body image issues, medical emergencies and financial insecurity. At the end of each chapter is a quality to embody, like perseverance, reflection and commitment, along with techniques my friends, colleagues and I have practiced. Consider them to be suggestions. Pick the ones you want to use or are drawn to, not the ones you feel you should do. We spend way too much time "shoulding" on ourselves!

Some of the recommended techniques are called "mudras." The common English meaning of the word *mudra* is "gesture" or "seal." Mudras are thought to have arisen spontaneously from the meditative states experienced by the ancient Indian sages. Mudras can be used to recognize a quality, attitude or energetic state that is already present and waiting to be awakened. You can think of mudras as a global positioning system (GPS) directing your energy to help you tune into the specific quality, attitude or energetic state you are working with.

Start your reading with the layer you are most comfortable with. Try one or more of the practices. How you choose to understand, personalize and apply any of the techniques to your life will be your choice alone. There is no single right way to do this. Your choices will not look, sound or feel like anyone else's because you are unique, just like a snowflake or a fingerprint.

And here's the key: the process can't be forced. Find your own way to ease into it. Be patient. Trust in yourself and the process. Reading about the enlightening up process of others will save you time, effort, money and tears.

For serious concerns or in an emergency, please seek professional help.

Your First Layer of Self-Awareness: Physical

The Taittiriya Upanishad, a 3,000-year-old East Indian wisdom tradition, states that our physical bodies are a manifestation of unity consciousness transmuted into matter.

This may seem esoteric and "out there" for many of us, but it does relate to two core questions we ask ourselves as we travel the self-awareness path. They are: "Who are we?" and "Where did we come from?"

The answers are deeper and more profound than, "We are human beings, and we're here because we were born." Your answer to those questions will differ depending on your understanding of both mysticism and science.

The Upanishads, like many of the world's ancient wisdom traditions, tell us we are spiritual beings having a human experience. It is based on the idea that existence begins with the concept of consciousness. Each of our layers devolves inward from the one above it. Then, with self-awareness (and a little grace), evolves outward as we enlighten up.

In the West, it's the opposite. Bodies come first. They are divided into systems, organs, tissues, molecules, atoms, cells, DNA and electromagnetic and bio-electric fields. Research tells us we are a combination of genetic imprinting and chemical processes that exist in a material world. Science assumes the mind and spirituality evolve from the physical body through the aging and learning process.

However, it is interesting to note that, as this research continues, scientists have encountered results they can't explain and that don't fit the current scientific consensus of how the body and mind are thought to work. Many are now talking to philosophers and mystics because there appear to be fascinating overlaps in the answers to those two core questions bridging the gap between East and West, and between mysticism and science. It is no longer either/or. It's inching closer to both/and.

In this contemporary treatment of the five-layer model, the first layer is comprised of two aspects: the body and the environment.

The Body

OUR BODY IS OUR SIZE, SHAPE, gender, health status, race and ethnicity. As human beings, we are complex and complicated right down to the smallest cell in our bodies. Although we appear to ourselves and others as a single unit, we are made of billions of microscopic parts organized into cells, tissues, organs and systems; each with its own job, working to keep us breathing and moving until structural challenges, health issues or death intervenes.

Most of us start our exploration of self-awareness with the body because it is visible and familiar. We begin by working with these important areas:

- body science
- optimal health
- social and cultural variables

Body Science

Anatomy, biology, physiology and kinesiology paint a picture of the human body at the physical level. We may not be drawn to study these sciences in-depth, but each of us can become aware of the miracles our bodies perform daily. We start by understanding the body's systems and what they do.

The number of systems varies depending on interpretation and the source consulted. But here is a list of the most commonly accepted ones:

- **Integumentary system:** The external layer of the body, including skin, hair, nails. Regulates body temperature; creates structure for sensation.

- **Skeletal system:** The framework and support of the body. Performs vital functions, such as protection, blood cell production, calcium storage and endocrine regulation.

- **Muscular system:** Maintains posture; aids in movement.

- **Nervous system:** Relays messages back and forth from the brain that affect the way we think, learn, move and behave.

- **Endocrine system:** Glands that secrete hormones and chemicals that regulate body activities.

- **Circulatory system:** Transports blood throughout the body and carries waste away from the cells.

- **Immune system:** Protects the body from pathogens and allergens.

- **Lymphatic system:** A part of the immune system that maintains fluid levels in the body, absorbs fats from the digestive tract, protects the body against foreign invaders, and removes cellular waste.

- **Respiratory system:** The lungs and other structures that carry oxygen to the body and the brain.

- **Digestive system:** Takes in food, digests it for absorption, then eliminates the rest as waste.

- **Urinary system:** Excretes waste; controls water and electrolyte balance in the body.

- **Reproductive system:** The organs and bodily structures that enable humans to reproduce.

All of us have imbalances in one or more of these systems. Our task in working with the body is to determine where they are in order to address them for optimal health and healing. Imbalances can show up in one or more of our body's systems. For example, an imbalance in the:

- musculoskeletal system may result in our image in the mirror showing us one shoulder or hip is higher than the other.

- immune system may cause us to get frequent colds, flu and bacterial infections.

- digestive system may show up as constipation, diarrhea or digestive upsets after eating.

A focus on optimal health is one way to identify and work with our imbalances.

Optimal Health

Optimal health is determined by the smooth functioning of these systems in relationship to each other. Each is rich in sensation, and our ability to be actively aware of these sensations determines the difference between responding appropriately when we sense that something feels off or reacting with anxiety or panic if we've ignored the messages until they morph from gentle whispers, like discomfort, to loud shouts indicating pain and illness.

The term "optimal health" means the best level of health we can achieve based on our situation. It is not limited to curing.

No matter our health status, we can heal. The word "healing" comes from the Anglo-Saxon word *hǣlen*, which means "to make whole, to have harmony and a sense of well-being in body, mind and spirit."

Curing is more about fixing problems, eradicating disease, and eliminating symptoms. People can be healed even if they are not cured and many can be cured without being healed. For example, those with a chronic disease can learn to accept and work with their physical condition to find healing and peace of mind. Conversely, people may have their physical condition fixed or cured but not realize healing on any level.

One noticeable effect of healing is a reduction in stress and anxiety, which in turn positively impacts our overall well-being. To recognize and work with this aspect of your first layer is crucial because your body is the vehicle that carries you through life.

Our health is determined by several factors including genetic inheritance, personal behaviors, access to quality healthcare, and our general external environment, such as the quality of air, water and housing conditions. Most of us want to be as healthy as possible for as long as possible. We start by taking care of our bodies, which can be tough to do in our body-conscious society.

How you see and feel about your body can have a direct influence, not only in how you view yourself, but also how you view and interact with others. If your goal is clarity, contentment and resilience, you will need to find a happy medium between the extremes of body fixation and unhealthy neglect. Working toward optimal health and healing in your first layer benefits the functioning of your other layers as well.

It's not hard to find information and guidelines on developing your self-care program, which will likely include recommendations for diet, exercise, adequate rest and a suggested schedule for medical, dental and vision check-ups. It's another thing entirely to grapple with resistance and "Just Do It" as the Nike slogan urges.

Sometimes it's the mind that says "Just Do It," but the body sends messages urging us to take a moment, think about how to do it, when to do it, and in what manner to do it for overall health and safety. Sometimes it's the body that says "Just Do It," and the mind sends messages to the body telling it there's too much work to do or there's not enough time. Then it may promise the body that you'll start next week or it broadcasts the unhelpful belief that "I'll never be perfect, so why try?" In either situation, employing self-awareness skills will help you negotiate peace and a balanced treaty between body and mind to make the right choices for your optimal health.

Like everything else in life, there are no guarantees, but as Benjamin Franklin once said, "An ounce of prevention is worth a pound of cure."

This advice is important, but the what, why and how much of each is personal. You have to determine what works best for you and not follow the latest diet fad, buy the newest fitness gadget, or enroll in every self-improvement program that comes along just because an expert says it will solve your problems.

Social and Cultural Variables

THE NATIONAL INSTITUTES OF HEALTH HAS documented a growing body of research on the association between social and cultural factors and health. Some of the variables reported are:[5]

- gender and sex roles.
- education levels.
- work environment and status.

5   LM Hernandez and DG Blazer (editors). "Genes, Behavior, and the Social Environment: Moving Beyond the Nature/Nurture Debate," *National Academies Press*, ncbi.nlm.nih.gov/books/NBK19924/. 2006, accessed December 4, 2020.

- physical and social environments.
- race and cultural background.
- social networks and support.
- personal beliefs and behavior.
- genetic inheritance.

For example, links between health, longevity, well-being and having a network of social support, including family, friends or groups, have been well established over the past thirty years. Our reactions and responses to how we work with our personal variables will have an impact on our interactions with our life, our world and our well-being.

The Environment

Then there is the second aspect of this layer, our environment, which includes our home, our communities and the planet.

We need to consider the environment as an aspect of this layer because philosophers and mystics have told us for centuries that "all is one." Hermes Trismegistus, an ancient Greek mystic, philosopher and author is quoted as saying:

> *As above, so below, as within, so without, as the universe, so the soul.*

This sentiment is now echoed by science as they consider that the boundary between our skin and our environment is permeable and a relative reality. The term "relative reality" is preferable to the word illusion, which, for me, has a connotation of "not real." Relative reality means that although the material world and its boundaries appear real and we function as if they are real, a greater, broader, deeper reality exists in which there are no boundaries.

Modern mystics, philosophers and scientists, especially theoretical physicists, recognize that underneath our material world and its solid appearance is a vast web of energy that binds everything, and everyone, together as one. Fritjof Capra explains in *The Tao of Physics*:

> *The more we penetrate into the submicroscopic*
> *world, the more we shall realize how the modern*
> *physicist, like the Eastern mystic, has come to see*
> *the world as a system of inseparable, interacting*
> *and ever-moving components with the observer*
> *being an integral part of this system.*[6]

When that profound statement sinks in, we can see the need to extend our self-awareness and self-care efforts toward the environment in which we live.

Climate Change

The Intergovernmental Panel on Climate Change's October 2019 special report was written and edited by ninety-one scientists from forty countries who analyzed more than six thousand scientific studies. It described a world of worsening food shortages, wildfires and a mass die-off of coral reefs as soon as 2040, a period well within the lifetimes of many of us who are alive today.[7]

Scientists and climate change activists aren't the only ones sounding the alarm about the need to pay attention to this issue. The late B. K. S. Iyengar, one of the world's most respected yogis, said:

> *...man is trying more and more to dominate*
> *the environment rather than control himself.*
> *Central heating, air conditioning, cars that we*
> *take out to drive three hundred yards, towns that*
> *stay lit up all night, and food imported from*

---

6   Fritjof Capra. *The Tao of Physics.* Shambhala Publications, Boston, MA, 2000.

7   Coral Davenport. "Major Climate Report Describes a Strong Risk of Crisis as Early as 2040." *The New York Times*, October 7, 2018, accessed November 11, 2020, nytimes.com/2018/10/07/climate/ipcc-climate-report-2040.html.

*around the world out of season are all examples
of how we try to circumvent our duty to adapt to
nature and instead force nature to adapt to us.*[8]

Personal Responsibility

IN RESPONSE, WE DO WHAT WE can to address this, but our good intentions don't always bring us the results we hoped for. For example, we recycle our plastics, paper, glass, cardboard, paperboard and cans, but ultimately we don't have control over what happens to our recyclables after we drop them into the recycling bin. That depends on a complicated intersection of marketing, business and governmental factors. Recycle anyway.

What you do have control over is your home environment. Exploring the connection between your personal environment and your well-being is a doable and worthwhile effort. In her book, *Healing Spaces*, medical researcher Dr. Esther Sternberg shares the dramatic results of Roger Ulrich's 1984 study on health and environment. Ulrich found that hospital patients with a view of nature healed faster than those without. Other studies indicate that live plants in your home and office or treasured items placed in strategic places can improve your mood and affect your immune system and physical health for the better.

Current mind-body research continues to study these connections and affirms the importance of a healthy and pleasing environment:

*Implicit in an understanding of the mind-
body connection is an assumption that physical
places that set the mind at ease can contribute to*

---

8   B.K.S. Iyengar. *Light on Life: The Yoga Journey to Wholeness, Inner Peace, and
Ultimate Freedom.* Rodale Books. Kindle edition.

> *well-being and those that trouble the emotions*
> *might foster illness.*[9]

It doesn't matter if you live in a mansion or a cold-water walk-up flat. Your home is where you eat, sleep and interact with partners, family, friends and pets. It is an extension of your interests. How you arrange your furniture, organize, decorate and clean your spaces and manage all of your stuff becomes an external reflection of your internal landscape. Your home and how you feel about it has an impact on your physical and mental well-being. How you care about your surroundings reflects how you care about the planet and the actions you take to care for it.

The first of the Nine Steps to Self-Awareness will help you deepen awareness of your body and your environment.

Step 1. Become Aware of Your Body and Your Environment

For Your Body

LEARN TO PAY ATTENTION TO YOUR physical body and how it moves and relates to the spaces around it. Use your five senses. What do you see? What can you hear? What can you smell and taste? What surfaces does your body touch?

Bring that awareness inside your body. Attune to the sensations you experience. Listen to the messages your body and all of its systems send.

For Your Environment

Pay attention to your environment and make as many positive changes as you can. Here are a few suggestions.

- If you have a green thumb, add a plant or two, or three.

---

9   Esther M. Sternberg, MD. *Healing Spaces.* Belknap Press, Harvard University, 2009.

- If keeping plants alive isn't in your DNA (it's so not in mine), try decorating with treasured items, symbols or mementos.
- Reduce clutter.
- Open windows to let in the fresh air.
- Play soft music to create a soothing sense of calm.

Do what you can to help the planet. This list of personal responsibility suggestions has been expanded from the older three "R's" of Reduce, Re-use and Recycle.

- Rethink your choices.
- Refuse single-use products.
- Reduce consumption.
- Refurbish old stuff.
- Repair before you replace.
- Re-use and reinvent; be creative.
- Recycle as the last option.

When we pay attention to our body and our environment, we are affecting our other four layers and the planet at the same time. If that sounds unbelievable, remember the butterfly effect put forth in 1963 by Edward Lorenz, a meteorology professor at MIT. In a mathematical calculation, he realized that tiny, butterfly-scale changes can have a significant and unpredictable impact on weather patterns. Essentially, what that meant is, a butterfly flapping its wings in Brazil could result in a hurricane in Texas. It's a powerful metaphor reinforcing the idea that small changes can have big consequences. The ancient wisdom traditions agree.

As you read the chapters in this section you will find personal stories about dealing with illness, living authentically, managing a healthy relationship with food, and understanding the attachments we have to our stuff. The practices at the end of each chapter provide

Enlighten Up!

"how to do it" exercises for acknowledging difficulty, practicing authenticity, paying attention, and embodying perseverance.

WHAT YOU SEE IS WHAT YOU GET

*Authenticity means erasing the gap between
what you firmly believe inside and what you
reveal to the outside world.*

— Adam Grant, PhD

==

Hair. What to do with it? Oh, the struggle! No matter what we do (fry it, dye it, buy it, tie it, twist it, mist it, curl it or unfurl it), we remain in a funk of discontent. Whether we consider it good hair, bad hair or barely-there hair, it's all too often *not* our crowning glory. But hair is a compelling element of the human condition and a larger than life first-layer fascination, fixation and opportunity for self-awareness and expressing one's authentic self.

A quick peek into history reveals that hair, in its many forms, styles, colors and shapes, can set fashion trends, define social status, and display or defy cultural norms. For example, to adhere to cultural or religious rules, men and women in many societies are required to cover their hair with some type of cloth. Or for an example of defiance, we can look back to the 1960s with the dawning of the

Age of Aquarius, the hippie counterculture revolution, and *Hair: The American Tribal Love-Rock Musical.*

Hair is symbolic of many aspects of human interaction. It is a symbol of strength in the biblical story of Samson and Delilah. When Delilah cut Samson's hair, he lost his strength and succumbed to his enemies. Western research on hair and its symbolic meanings dates back to Sigmund Freud and Charles Berg who theorized that the unconscious symbolism of hair was related to castration anxiety. Anthropologists, ethnographers and other scholars continue to study the significance of hair across the globe in places like Europe, India, Samoa, Africa, Turkey and, of course, the United States. Included in many research studies is the connection between the standards of female beauty and hair.

Hair is a larger-than-life first-layer issue, especially for Black women. Don't believe me? Just ask one. We've struggled with the issue of hair ever since our enslaved ancestors arrived on America's shores where our curly and kinky hair was deemed inferior and used as a justification for seeing us as sub-human. We still have issues, but in today's world, changes and personal choices are plentiful. My issue with the mop on my head was (notice I say "was") tied up with feelings of not being authentic, and I wanted to be authentic.

That was my goal. Yet I struggled unsuccessfully to reach it. I was trained from childhood to present the image of a good girl; well-behaved, high heels, business suit hemmed below the knee, and that little scarf tied at my neck to be sure no cleavage showed. This is what I presented to the world for years. This, according to everything I'd absorbed from family and society, would make me acceptable. But that wasn't who I felt myself to be on the inside. The key to making the outside match the inside started with my hair.

I am happy to report that after years of struggling with decades of bad hair days, I finally had a good hair day that's lasted since the early '90s. Of course, that eventful day started as a bad hair day with too much humidity, too much kink, and too much hair. I was on vacation with friends on Martha's Vineyard, and I'd found the perfect summer bad hair day hat in Oak Bluffs. It was planted firmly over my untamed bush, truce time between my hair and me.

Ti, Norma and I (I've changed their names to protect both the innocent and the guilty) were relaxing on the sun-drenched deck of Norma's summer home. We'd been vacationing together for several years; same time, same place, same faces. We were settling in for a morning of "island time." With little or no relationship to the clock, time on the Vineyard can slow you down to a snail's pace and engulf you in a pleasant vacuum that refreshes your spirit.

My impression of Ti was that of a superwoman who could manage an impressive schedule of cocktail parties and club meetings, keep her house operating-room sterile, and pull off a sit-down dinner for twelve without breaking a sweat. I admired her. She was always in control. If there were cracks in that smooth façade, I couldn't see them.

All of a sudden, she turned in my direction and said, "Beth, I think you'd look cute with short hair."

"Nah, I don't think so."

My refusal fell on deaf ears. She turned and dragged Norma into the conversation. Norma is the kind of people person who devotes her life to good food, good books, and sweatshirts with catchy slogans. The one she had on that day read, "Beware! I'm retired. I know it all and have plenty of time to tell you about it." She turned her Revlon-red grin in my direction and told Ti exactly where she could find scissors and a towel.

I put up a weak resistance. Ti was insistent, telling me she had run a hair salon out of her dorm room to help pay college tuition. I could feel myself begin to waffle. What would one more hair disaster mean in the context of years of hair disasters? I shrugged and said, "Okay."

Ti returned with scissors and towel in hand. Norma moved a deck chair into a hair-cutting position for Ti and then made a front-row spot for herself. They both eyeballed me.

My heart beat faster. Time slowed and images of my hair wars flashed before my eyes. They began with pigtails and red plaid ribbons that took me through elementary school. I hated them. They were not the signature of someone who was smart, stylish and had a witty personality. When I looked into the mirror, that is who I saw staring back at me. Pigtails didn't cut it.

Throughout my childhood, when I blew out the candles on my birthday cake, I wished for one thing—straight hair. When I prayed at night for the health and safety of my parents, and reluctantly for that of my little brother, I always added a postscript to God for straight hair. I was convinced that if God could help me find the right shampoo or conditioner, a miracle could be had, and I'd be able to toss my head and flip long straight hair over my shoulders just like the movie stars. With that miracle, I knew the outside me would match the inside me.

No such luck. In junior high school, I exchanged my Dick Clark American Bandstand ponytail for a pageboy, which was achieved through sheer torture. The smell of Dixie Peach Pomade and hot comb smoke permeated our kitchen every other Saturday night. Yes, my hair was straight but only temporarily. I learned to hate swimming and to fear rainy days. Water would make my hair "go back," and then I'd have to go through that peculiar kind of hell all over again. Yes, it would flip, but it was too heavy to really toss. I did not look or feel smart, stylish or witty.

My first perm came just in time for senior week and graduation. It made my hair straight and kept it that way. What a relief! A battle won! Off to college I went with a suitcase full of hair maintenance equipment: special shampoo and conditioner, rollers, Dippity-do hair gel, endpapers, clips, rat tail combs and a big bonnet hairdryer. At last, I had the kind of long straight hair I'd dreamed about.

I tossed my head and flipped my hair, but to my dismay and disappointment, it did not express my smarts, style or wit. I couldn't understand it. I now saw that self looking back at me in the mirror, but she wasn't reflected in my hair. I was at a loss.

Marriage came next, along with motherhood. I was suddenly too busy to worry about my hair and too tired to think about being smart, stylish and witty. I wanted simple and easy. The Afro had arrived, and in political solidarity with the Civil Rights Movement (and because my hair was thinning and breaking from constant perms—yes, I see the irony), I switched to a 'fro. A *big* 'fro. A supersized Angela Davis 'fro.

My husband was very upset I no longer had long straight hair. My mother couldn't understand why I'd want to leave my house "with all those naps on top of your head." They judged me by my hair. Well, why not? Hadn't I linked my identity to it for years? And don't Black folks have a centuries-old love-hate relationship with hair? Good hair being straight, and bad hair being nappy? Confused, I wore my Afro defiantly, walked softly, and carried a big pick.

During my 30-something dress-for-success years, I found myself divorced and desperate for a makeover. So, I packed my top bureau drawer with rollers in different sizes, as well as a blow dryer with an array of attachments, styling combs, brushes, curling irons, mousses, gels and hairsprays. With each new hair product featured in *Ebony* or *Essence,* hope sprang eternal that I'd find hair that truly fit the "me" I was inside. No such luck.

I thought briefly about cornrows or dreadlocks but did not have the chutzpah. I married again, and as I moved through step-parenting and menopause, I declared a cease-fire between my *not* crowning glory and me. I elected to accept the fact there might not ever be a hair match. And so the truce remained in effect until its demise, which can be laid directly at the feet of my second husband.

I'd gone shopping. It had been a great day; all the right stuff at all the right prices. One outfit, in particular, I loved. It was a dark burgundy cotton knit. The harem pants had a flattering cut. The top was a cropped, asymmetrical jacket with no collar. It was stylish in a global, ethnic, artsy way that matched the inside me.

I decided to model it for hubby. I strode into the den where he was glued to the TV. I placed my smart, stylish and witty self squarely between him and his Saturday afternoon testosterone contest. "Well, whaddya think?"

He said, "Well, it's you. I can see that, but" he paused, "now don't take this the wrong way," he paused again, took a deep breath and plunged ahead, "Hon, your hair just doesn't match your outfit."

Just like that, the cease-fire was over. The war between me and my hair was underway once more.

This time, Ti held the power. I looked from Ti to Norma and back. Ti flicked the towel and clicked the scissors. Norma's manicured fingers tap, tap, tapped the back of the deck chair. A long pause followed. And into that pause, I said, "Do it."

As Ti began to cut, I gave myself completely to the moment. Delicious. I should have been terrified, but I wasn't. I heard the snip, snip, snip of the scissors and watched with curious detachment as brown, wooly clumps the size of golf balls fell onto the white terrycloth towel around my shoulders. Norma was at full attention. Her eyes sparkled. This was high drama.

"I'm going to shape it to your head," Ti said. "It'll be really short in back, but you'll have enough on top to set in small rollers for a little curl. Now, it'll probably take you a little time to get used to it, so don't be upset when you look in the mirror."

I didn't like the tentative tone in her voice, and I didn't like the sinking feeling creeping into my gut. The snips and clips continued.

I felt panic slide in. What had I agreed to? I shifted from panic to catatonic.

A few snips later, Ti straightened up, put the scissors on the table, and proclaimed, "There! I think you should go shampoo, pick your hair out, and let me clip the stray ends. Then we'll put a few rollers in the front and you'll be all set." Her fingers patted here and fluffed there. She leaned over my shoulder. "Now don't hate me if you don't like it, okay?"

I nodded weakly. My knees shook as I stood up. I planned to dash to the bathroom, have a private fit, and then get myself under control. The sliding glass door to the kitchen was closed, and I caught a glimpse of my reflection as I turned to get up. My breath caught in my throat, my jaw dropped, and shivers ran up my spine. I was overwhelmed, bowled over, ecstatic and more than pleased. I matched. Inside and out! I clapped my hands.

"Ti, it's wonderful!"

"Oh, good. Then you like it?" Ti looked relieved.

"Like it? I love it. It's me. It's really me! Who knew?" I hugged Ti and Norma, then dashed off to the bathroom to shampoo, pick and grab a few rollers out of Ti's yellow curler bag.

Imagine. All that time, money and energy spent on products, procedures, professionals and internal struggle with no satisfactory results. In the end, all it took to match my inner view of myself to the outer expression was the unfolding of time, good friends, and a pair of old kitchen scissors.

Shortly after that, I wrote this poem.

My Good Hair Day
I look in the mirror and what do I see
On top of my head looking back at me?
Protein strands, kinky, short and fat.
It's called my hair, how 'bout that?

Some easy passes with my pick
A few pats of the hand done real quick
No muss, no fuss, I'm set for the day
My hair and I match. Hip, hip hooray!

This journey may have started with my hair, but it most certainly did not end there. Today, I have come to understand that having my inside and outside match is not about hair at all. It's about feeling, being and acting authentically in a way that balances all five layers of self-awareness. I just didn't realize it, and the conflict I felt was created by the inconsistencies between the beliefs, feelings, thoughts and values I held inside and the actions I took as a result of them.

Inconsistencies are especially troublesome if you are not aware of them (and I wasn't) or when awareness brings them to the surface, especially if the desire to adhere to external factors, like social status and cultural norms, blocks changes. In my case, it was the cultural norms of beauty and acceptance despite being an "other" (Black and female in a predominately white male culture). If I'd had the necessary self-awareness to realize that, I might have been able to acknowledge my inconsistencies, figure things out, deal with the imbalance between my inner truth and outer mask, and find the courage to tell everyone, "What you see is what you get!"[10] Better late than never.

Now, if you have come to a comfortable place with your inner self and its outer expression, you've probably found answers to questions like:

- How do others see me?
- How do I see myself?
- How concerned am I with how others see me?

---

10   The catch phrase of Flip Wilson's sassy, liberated drag persona, Geraldine Jones, from his 1970s comedy show. You can still find a number of Flip/Geraldine sketches on YouTube.

- Does something need to change?
- If I make changes to be fully authentic, how might others receive them?
- How will I feel if the reaction is negative? Positive? Neutral?

If you have started asking these questions, you've accomplished a lot. Pat yourself on the back. If not, you have some work to do, if you choose to. (No pressure!)

As you find your answers, keep these suggestions in mind.

- Accept the answers you find without judgment.
- Understand they may change as you change; be flexible.
- Don't compare yourself to others. This is hard. Find ways to work around it.
- Be sure any changes you make are made because they help you be more like you and not like someone else.
- If you find an external or internal attribute can't be changed, accept it, manage it and embrace it as part of who you authentically are.

Sometimes you may find that the pull comes from wanting your outside to match your inside, and sometimes it's the inside that wants to match the outside. Be very clear about which is the stronger pull for you. Disconnects between your inner self and its outer expression can get complicated and result in imbalances in one or more of your five layers. If you doubt that, just ask anyone who identifies as transgender or someone who is outwardly a ten on the "wow she/he is hot" scale but who has serious self-esteem issues. Being authentic has little to do with standards of beauty and acceptance, and more to do with finding a way to be 100 percent authentic and comfortable in your own skin.

Finally, it's important to understand that the answers you find may be very different from the answers your friends, family and social groups may find for themselves or wish for you. No one key fits all locks.

Practice: Find Your Sweet Spot
Quality to Embody: Authenticity

BEING YOUR AUTHENTIC SELF REQUIRES FINDING clarity between who you are internally and how you interact with others. Like self-awareness, authenticity is a state, not a trait. The process of determining what your authentic self is can be confusing, amusing, defining, surprising, inviting and exciting. It can slice you and dice you and put you back together again. It will ebb and flow, shift and change depending on the situation. But to my way of thinking, it does have a core, a sweet spot, which is a deeply felt sense of knowing. In the search for authenticity, you have a right to be yourself and a responsibility to be accepting of others.

Your Right

I have the right to acknowledge and embrace my authentic self.

Matching your external behavior to your internal truth is easier said than done, and not always possible, but here are three indicators of authenticity.

- You are able to say what you mean and mean what you say.
- You accept yourself as you are, warts and all—nobody's perfect.
- You are living much of your life with moment-to-moment self-awareness because "The past is history, tomorrow's a mystery, today is a gift, that's why they call it the present."[11]

---

11 The Family Circus newspaper cartoon from August 31, 1994, attributed to Bill Keane.

When you are feeling deeply authentic, you may experience a sense of calm, ease, free-flowing energy, or a sense of expansion. When this happens, there is nothing to do but relax and enjoy it.

Your Responsibility

I have a responsibility to be aware of and to manage my actions in situations where I can't be 100 percent authentic.

There are always circumstances where being wholly authentic can be difficult, not advisable, or even impossible. Here are a few examples.

- You are in a meeting, making a presentation you have worked on for months, and are being interrupted with objections before you can finish sharing your ideas.
- You are an hourly worker being hassled by your boss.
- You are trying to remain calm at Thanksgiving dinner with your family, who disapprove of your lifestyle and your politics.

If you are unable to respond authentically in these situations, you may feel shut down and blocked. Before you respond or react, tune into your body and watch for sensations. Everyone is different, but some common sensations in difficult situations might be a headache, a clenched jaw, shallow breathing, digestive upsets, or back pain. Tuning into body sensations helps you connect to the state of your five layers so you can consciously choose an appropriate response that might ease or shift the situation. If that doesn't work, you can take some long deep breaths to relieve your stress and patiently wait it out until you can leave.

Remember, your search for authenticity will take time, focus and patience. There will be challenges along the way, but finding your sweet spot needs to be at the top of your daily to-do list.

STUFF

Stuff. The process of enlightening up has real relevance when it comes to our material possessions. By examining how and why we think, feel and behave with, for and about our stuff, we can see how interrelated, interconnected and intertwined our five layers of self-awareness are.

Layer 1: Physical

WE ALL HAVE STUFF. OUR LIVES are filled with stuff. It fills our rooms, attics, basements, garages, backyard sheds and storage units. At some point, most of us will be faced with the need to do something about all the stuff we have lovingly (out of necessity or compulsion) collected and stored.

There are many ways to think and feel about stuff. Some of us can't stand the thought of being surrounded by any more stuff than we can comfortably fit into our home. Others of us give up all but the most essential stuff to live spartan lives in an ashram, intentional community or other alternate lifestyle. Still others never feel like they have enough stuff, and some are unable to let anything go even when keeping stuff leads to an unhealthy environment.

Starting with our hands-on relationship with our stuff is an easier place to begin unraveling why we view stuff the way we do. So a good question to ask ourselves is: How much of what I own is the right stuff and how much is stuff and nonsense?

What we surround ourselves with is often directly related to our physical comfort or discomfort. We need stuff to live in our five-sense material world and having at least some stuff (like clothes, shoes, water, food and a place to sleep) is necessary. If these things are absent or lacking, we experience a great deal of discomfort. Consider the plight of the homeless or victims of war and disaster.

Start by considering how much and what kind of stuff has followed you through life. I track mine through my moves—eleven of them thus far in my life.

1. From a modest middle-class home filled with my parents' stuff to college with enough stuff to fill one-half of a small dorm room.

2. My college dorm to a room at the YWCA, where I brought everything from the dorm with me except for a few boxes of paper and books that eventually molded away in my parents' basement.

3. The YWCA to an apartment with two roommates; everything fit, no issues. I had a nice-sized bedroom, one-third of the refrigerator, and use of the kitchen. The living room was

filled with my roommates' stuff. It was heaven for a young working girl.

4. The apartment and roommates to first marriage and two years as an army wife in Germany. We lived on the economy (that's army-speak for not living on the base). We had a furnished apartment and a German landlady. I was able to bring two trunks of clothes, shoes and my pots and pans.

5. From Germany to a duplex in the United States with hubby and baby. At last, I could buy furniture and accumulate real grown-up stuff.

6. The duplex to homeownership in a raised ranch with hubby, toddler and more stuff.

7. From the raised ranch and divorce to an apartment with a toddler and just enough stuff to fill each room.

8. From the apartment to homeownership of a small Cape Cod house as a singleton with a school-aged child and not enough stuff to fill it. That didn't last long. I had a blast painting, purchasing and designing my new space.

9. My small Cape Cod to a 2,500-square-foot house on a lake with second hubby and much new stuff to fill it.

10. The huge home to a small apartment after my second husband died from brain cancer and I dealt with financial difficulty. (That's a story for a different time.) A lifetime of stuff from the attic, basement and garage was put into storage.

11. The small apartment to a slightly larger condo with no attic, basement, garage or yard. Most of the stuff in storage was given away to friends, sold, donated or junked. That felt like a much-needed cleansing, an emptying, and a huge burden lifted. I was firm in my commitment to have in the condo only what would comfortably fit. No storage facility, cube or shed, now or in the future.

As you can see, I'm in the "can't stand the thought of being surrounded by any more stuff than we can comfortably fit into our homes" group. I anticipate one more move, from my condo to a cremation jar. I will not be taking any of my stuff with me. Please laugh. I am!

Layer 2: Energetic

THE AMOUNT OF STUFF WE DEAL with can have a direct relationship to our physical and mental energy. I can feel my energy expand or contract in certain spaces.

When my living space gets cluttered, as it can do when I'm juggling a variety of projects, my brain fogs, my energy gets depleted and scattered, and I have trouble focusing. When I get around to straightening up, my energy stabilizes, and the brain fog clears. A certain amount of clutter, disorder or chaos in my home is okay. I can handle it for about a week or two. When I notice the energy drain and the arrival of the heebie-jeebies, I know it's time to clean up, straighten up, and organize stuff to free my energy until the next time. It's a cycle. I persevere.

Our stuff defines us, tells us stories about ourselves, and also tells visitors to our home who we are and what we value.

When I visit spaces that are light, bright, open and well-organized, I can feel my energy expand. I feel light, bright, open and ready to engage with everything and everyone who is occupying that space with me.

It's the opposite in cluttered spaces. When I find myself in these spaces, I can feel my energy contract. Maybe it's too much furniture in a small room, overstuffed closets with doors that can't completely close, or kitchen counters piled high with appliances, dishes and stacks of unopened mail. I try not to judge, but I'm not always successful. When judgments flood in, they look like this:

- How can people live like this?
- Can't they see the clutter?
- Doesn't it bother them?
- How do they function?
- This place would look so much better if they'd just...

Fortunately, I have enough self-discipline to keep my mouth shut. When I leave, the first thing I do is take a long deep breath and shake off my discomfort.

Layer 3: Mental

THE TROUBLE WITH STUFF IN THIS layer begins with the word "attachment." As you can see, I have a mental and emotional attachment issue around clutter. I have enough self-awareness to recognize it, admit it, and accept that the emotional charge is real. I think my reaction has a lot to do with the way I think and feel about stuff. Understanding this gives me some clarity. Obviously, I am not going to stop visiting my friends, but when I'm consciously aware of my issues about their stuff, it affects me less and decreases my discomfort.

No matter how much or how little we have, we have attachments to our stuff. If we didn't, there would be no need to buy stuff, collect stuff, place stuff, store stuff, or find ways to get rid of it.

It's in this layer where we explore our attachments to stuff and, if needed, work toward a pattern of healthy attachment. A too-strong or too-wrong attachment to keeping or releasing stuff can lead to hoarding or its opposite, obsessive-compulsive cleaning. Both conditions are considered expressions of obsessive-compulsive disorder.

The Mayo Clinic describes a hoarding disorder as a persistent difficulty in discarding or getting rid of items because of a perceived need to save them. If you can stand to watch reality TV shows about hoarders (I can't), you see this type of attachment to stuff is unhealthy.

I'll bet most of us know someone who is a hoarder, maybe you even have one in your family. I have one in mine. For years, I wondered why I was never invited to their home. A family member admitted to me that newspapers, magazines and books were stacked so high on the stairs and in the hallways, that there was barely a body-wide path to navigate through the rooms.

The other end of the scale is obsessive-compulsive cleaning. It takes decluttering to the extreme. People who suffer from this condition actually experience physical symptoms, like anxiety, insomnia, the jitters, or tightness in the chest, that last until they sort, rearrange, declutter and clean. That helps for a little while, but the relief does not last. It's another manifestation of an unhealthy attachment to stuff.

Most of us, thankfully, are somewhere in the middle of these extreme ends of the spectrum. And that means we can figure out for ourselves how to manage our stuff and not let it manage us. Understanding our attachments to stuff and knowing when to discard, release, change, keep or give it away can be enlightening both literally and figuratively.

Nina is a colleague who has written about how she tackles her stuff. It became an issue in her life after her parents and her husband's parents died. A lot of their stuff ended up in Nina's home. She found some things useful and kept them. Others, they gave away.

However, she found a lot of the stuff wasn't useful, but it still held strong emotional power over her; things like samples of her father's graphic design work, scrapbooks her husband's mother created, and some of her mother's fashionable clothes Nina knows she'll never wear. Releasing these things was difficult. She'd open a box and look through it. Then, memories and emotions popped up. She'd feel overwhelmed, close the box, and leave it. Of that process, she wrote:

> *About a year ago, I started a practice of getting rid of at least one thing every day. I kept it up for a few months. In the beginning, it was easy because every time I opened a cabinet I saw something of my own that I really didn't need. But then it became harder and harder. I would open a box of my parent's stuff, feel overwhelmed with emotion, and then close it again.*

This put an end to discarding one thing a day until she came to understand why.

Layer 4: Intuitive Wisdom

EXPERIENCE AND SELF-REFLECTION CAN POINT US to why we feel the way we do about our stuff. After engaging her witness, Nina realized it was not the items themselves she was attached to but the memories and emotions they called up. With that flash of self-awareness, she was able to move forward and go back to discarding one item a day.

It also helps to understand how we feel about items we are strongly attached to and how we'd react if we lost them or gave them up.

Recently, I got an email from my son, which I thought was strange because he usually communicates by texting. His message was, "I forgot my phone at home today. Mixed feelings. Kinda naked. Kinda blissful detachment. Interesting."

My response was, "Enjoy the moment of self-awareness."

A few days later, it happened to me. I emailed him with the words "my turn" in the subject line. "I left my phone at home yesterday and didn't have music for my yoga class. Experienced a flash of panic and then calm acceptance."

He replied, "Acceptance is much easier on the nerves."

Clearly, my son is a wise man.

Forgetting or misplacing a cell phone is one thing. Losing a phone or wallet, or the keys to your car or house, would definitely be more distressing. I can't even imagine what it would feel like to be homeless or a victim of war or a disaster. Of course, I don't equate losing a phone, wallet or keys to those desperate situations, but I'm hopeful that being able to clearly witness our reactions to losses, both small and large, will enable to us to respond with some measure of calmness despite the discomfort we feel.

Sometimes, we can experience a delayed attachment reaction to items we happily give up. A few years ago, I decided to buy a new car and give my 2000 Subaru (named Miss Kitty because she purrs) to my great-niece who was turning sixteen. The thought of Miss Kitty being junked was an unacceptable option. Giving the car to my niece would prevent that. It would benefit my niece and stay in the family, a triple-win for Miss Kitty, my niece and me.

The decision was easy, but giving the car away was something else entirely. I was kind of stunned at how I felt a few weeks later when I drove to her dad's house to drop off the car. I felt like I was losing a friend. For sixteen years, Miss Kitty had carried me through heartbreaks, disappointments, health challenges, long trips and bad weather. My breath caught in my throat as I gave my niece the keys and, for a longer time than I'm comfortable admitting, every time I saw that model car on the road, I'd feel the loss in my gut. I had to recognize an emotional attachment I hadn't realized I had, then work on letting it go.

Loss of stuff, relationships, behaviors, health and ultimately life itself is inevitable. I think finding a healthy attachment to our stuff is not about how much stuff we have but how emotionally attached to it we are. Our level of attachment affects our reactions and response to a loss. Is this an easy practice? No. Is it worth working on? Absolutely.

Layer 5: Bliss

THERE ARE POINTS IN LIFE WHEN dealing with our stuff looms large. That's when downsizing is necessary because we've decided to live in smaller, more easily maintained spaces, like apartments, condos, tiny houses or retirement communities.

It can be somewhat daunting to look at a lifetime of stuff we've accumulated. Stuff we need, stuff we've inherited, and stuff we want, like collections of stamps, currency, dolls, trading cards and comic books. But when we come face-to-face with our attachments, we realize the need to let go.

Letting go of stuff, or anything else, is a process you will face at all stages of life. If you practice consciously letting go in small ways, you will be better prepared for the bigger challenges of dealing with difficult attachments to thoughts, emotions, relationships, habits and behaviors.

An exercise that might help with the struggle of what to keep or let go is called "Lost it in the fire." It asks you to imagine your house burned down and everything you've accumulated, treasured or consider irreplaceable is lost. When confronted with the decision of how to release items that are not necessary, but that retain strong emotional attachments, ask yourself, "What if I lost this in a fire?" Then you can recognize your attachments and decide what to do about them with full awareness.

Practice: Three Steps to
Manage Attachments to Stuff

Quality to Embody: Perseverance

BARRING A SERIOUS CONDITION, LIKE HOARDING or obsessive-compulsive cleaning, your emotional bond or attachment to an item is a need to treasure, store or hold onto it. If you are attached to more stuff than you are comfortable with, you need to discover why.

Try these three steps for recognizing, accepting and working through your emotional attachment to your stuff.

INSTRUCTIONS

1. **Check yourself.** Answer the following questions.

   * How do I feel about people who have more stuff than I do?

   * How do I feel about people who have much less than I do?

   * If something happened and I lost everything, how would I feel? What would I replace?

   * If I buy something new, can I let go of something I already have?

   * Do I have a hard time letting go of stuff? If so, why? If not, why not?

2. **Take inventory.** If you have stuff in an attic, basement or storage facility, survey one area at a time and take a hard look at the contents. Do you really need everything? Are you keeping things because they evoke memories or have an emotional pull, or do you feel obligated to hold onto them? Try Nina's technique of ridding yourself of one item a day by selling, donating or giving it away. Then see how you're doing in six months.

3. **Make conscious choices.** It's important to our self-awareness journey to have a conscious understanding of our emotional attachments to the things we surround ourselves with. Once we have that, we make better decisions about what to keep, what to donate or give away, and what we absolutely need to hold onto. In this way, we are managing our stuff rather than it managing us.

There's a Zen proverb that reminds us how important this is. The proverb states simply, "Let go or be dragged." I think that says it all.

FOOD, A WEIGHTY ISSUE

Mindful eating isn't linear. It's more like a
spiral taking you deeper into knowing how to
care for yourself.

— Michelle May, MD

"Food, glorious food." This song was sung by a group of hungry orphans in the movie, *Oliver*. They were obsessed with food because they had so little of it and what they had was pretty awful. Like many of us, I am obsessed with food—reading about it, cooking it, watching shows about it and, most of all, eating it.

If you need more proof about our nation's obsession with food, stop by the cookbook section in any bookstore. You will find beautiful pictures and instructions for preparing mouth-watering appetizers, entrées and desserts. Then search the internet and find thousands of recipes and advice on what to eat, what not to eat, how much to eat, when and where to eat, and how to lose the weight gained from all that eating.

It's overwhelming, but a healthy dose of nonjudgmental self-awareness becomes a useful tool in our first-layer experience with food. Our goal is to find ways to consciously pay attention to our food likes, dislikes, impulses and fears. This gives us real power over our choices and enhances self-care. Engaging with food in this way will help us lose weight, put it on, maintain it, or seek help with serious issues, like eating disorders.

What we eat and what eats us are two sides of this topic. We need to pay attention to both sides. Let's start with what we eat. The process boils down to this:

- **Ingestion:** Eating—the fun part. Our food journey begins in the mouth. After we chew and chomp, it slides down the esophagus and into the stomach, where digestion begins.

- **Digestion and absorption:** The small and large intestines further break down the food, absorb essential nutrients, and send them into the bloodstream to nourish the body.

- **Elimination:** Any leftover undigested food matter is eliminated regularly by our (hopefully) efficient disposal system.

What eats us comes from relationships, work, finances, health, the environment and a variety of other sources. It all percolates throughout our layers.

Here's how the process works in the mind-space (our third layer).

- **Ingestion:** We have a front-row seat at the buffet table of life to the good, the bad, the beautiful, and the ugly.

- **Digestion and absorption:** What we take in is sifted and stirred and simmered through our thoughts, emotions and core beliefs. Then it's absorbed, blended and processed through all five layers by our perceptions, habits, reactions and responses. We're usually fine about digesting, absorbing and storing the beautiful and the good. It's the bad and the ugly that cause problems and pain.

- **Elimination:** Difficulty resolving and releasing unhelpful attachments to the bad and the ugly can result in emotional blockages that often lead to physical problems, like constipation, indigestion and diarrhea.

My relationship with what I eat and what eats me is like a tossed salad—lots of ingredients mixed together and dressed with my "it is what it is" story. It's just as long-term and complex as anyone else's. Although we may have similar experiences on the path to a healthy relationship with what we eat and what eats us, there are always individual rest stops, breakdowns and detours.

"Everybody is somebody's lunch." I don't know where I read or heard that, but my understanding about life and my relationship with food is centered on that line. Here are some vignettes on how it plays out.

Years ago, I met the gardener at the New Age Health Spa in Neversink, New York. I was there for a weekend spa vacation. At meals, it was common for staff and visitors to eat together in the dining room. One day during lunch, the gardener told us he was quitting. We all wanted to know why. In so many words, he told us he loved his job, digging into the earth, feeling the dirt in his hands, working with the plants and vegetables, and watching them grow. Then he sighed and admitted he was tired of hearing the lettuce scream when he picked it.

That sounded strange then, but science had begun studying plant communication and had discovered that plants do indeed communicate. So the gardener's experience may not have been as whacky as it first sounded.

In any case, we eat living things and, when we die, living things eat us. As a kid, my friends and I sang this weird little rhyme with relish:

The worms go in and the worms go out
The worms play pinochle on your snout

Your tummy turns an icky green
And looks and tastes just like whipped cream

Imagine my surprise when I discovered this concept in the Taittirya Upanishad from 3,000 years ago.

From food are made all bodies, which become
Food again for others after their death.

Whoa! With that confirmation of my childhood rhyme in mind, I try to follow the Native American practice—to be thankful and express gratitude for anything that gives up its life to nourish mine, from lettuce to fried oysters to my latest experiment with a sustainable protein source—crickets, commonly known as "land shrimp."

Our food choices are important. We are encouraged to eat healthy, unprocessed food when possible and adopt a regular exercise schedule to keep our systems in balance and functioning well. But what does that mean?

It means that it's different for each of us and it has to be because what we choose to eat for optimal health is ultimately based on our individual needs. It takes attention, clarity and self-awareness to know what that is: to do what works, to stick to it for as long as it works, and to be flexible about changing it when it no longer works.

Of course, sticking to what works is the hard part. There is so much to tempt and distract us. And don't get me started on dieting, another national obsession. My mom spent her life in a holy war against fat and fat people. She fat-shamed anyone she thought was overweight, including me. I became a target after the birth of my son. When the baby weight hung on, I heard about it through many silent side-eye glances and sly remarks about the size of my ass.

That's when the dieting began. I've tried all the famous ones: Atkins, South Beach, The Zone Diet, calorie counting, vegetarianism, The Master Cleanse, intermittent fasting, and Sugar Busters.

Did any of them work? Sure—some better than others, but nothing stuck. My experience with vegetarianism was probably the least successful.

I read the books. I was careful to get the nutrients I needed from both food and supplements, but despite my efforts, I was always tired, my skin was dry, and I was frequently sick with colds. Then I read *Eat Right for Your Type*, which linked choices about what to eat to your blood type. Was it scientifically sound? I don't know. Did it make sense to me? At the time, yes, it did. I was desperate to try anything. As blood type O positive, the suggestion was to eat meat. I added fish and chicken back into my diet. In a couple of weeks, my body thanked me and I felt like a new person.

Today, I don't diet and I don't count calories. I eat to be healthy, not to lose weight. My guide is my digestive system. For me, that means careful food combining and eliminating most (but not all) dairy, beans and grains. To my utter surprise, I lost those extra pounds without even trying. I do not promote or suggest my eating style will work for you. I only know it's working for me. How did I achieve this food wisdom? I closely watched what happened in my body from ingestion to digestion, absorption and ultimately elimination.

For most of my life, my relationship with food started from the front end, eating. Now my relationship with food is based on what happens at the other end; how I digest food and how easily and regularly I poop. Put another way, it depends on my digestive fire, the force at the source.

When I was younger, I could digest rocks, but now I have to be more careful about what I eat. The issues in my digestive tissues, which started after menopause, are or were indigestion, hemorrhoids and occasional constipation.

This issue became very personal a few years ago and was driven home not by what I read, heard or thought but by paying attention to what my body had to say. It spoke loud and clear, and there was no ignoring what it was telling me.

I thought I was having a heart attack: chest pressure, stomach pain, clammy sweat, nausea, etc. I drove myself to an emergency medical walk-in center, where they listened to my symptoms, put me in an ambulance, and sent me to a local hospital where I was admitted. Over the next several hours, I was put through every cardiac test they had. All of them indicated my heart was fine. They did not offer any possible reasons for my symptoms. Perhaps because of hospital policies they could not. I don't know.

After an overnight stay, I was released and went home with no answers. It was only after I did my own research, along with a few similar but less severe experiences, that I came to realize I was now lactose intolerant. I was not a happy camper! I love ice cream, cheese and yogurt, but I accepted my new reality and thankfully I have found acceptable substitutes.

My digestive system has also informed me it no longer likes beer. On the bright side, if there is a bright side to not being able to drink a cold frothy glass of beer, I can cook with it. It's especially good in chili, BBQ and gravy.

Now the choices about what, when and how to eat are made to support the functioning of my digestive system, period. Any other health benefits, like weight loss, are side effects.

Then there's the poop factor. Fortunately for me, my elimination is similar to my mother's. Like clockwork, she had a bowel movement first thing in the morning, every morning. This remained a pattern for her until she passed away at the age of 102. It is true for me too, but occasionally it isn't. When my son was born, the stress of being a wife, a new mom, and a working woman did throw things off balance from time to time. Missing a day or two raised the yellow caution flag, but when one or two days became three or more, the red flag of alarm and discomfort flew high and remained until it resolved itself or I took a laxative.

I also experienced constipation during the holidays. Given the changes in my daily routine, it's not surprising. There were social gatherings with family and friends (functional and dysfunctional), changes in diet (more sugar, alcohol, fat and carbs), and a decrease in exercise (along with time-worn excuses: the gym is closed; the gym is open, but I'm too tired; my to-do list is too long; etc.). Then there was holiday shopping in crowded malls with loud Muzak and driving in heavy traffic, or dealing with crowded airports and long security lines.

Stress and the changes that happen with aging and daily living will often manifest themselves physically in your digestive process. When your body tells you to make changes in your relationship with food or life experiences, pay attention.

Practice: Manage What You Eat and What Eats You
Quality to Embody: Attentiveness

IF YOU WANT TO MANAGE WHAT you eat and what eats you, start with your digestive system. When it is in balance, all your layers, at least theoretically, should reflect that balance as well. To better support the digestive process (for both food and life experiences), it helps to think of the phrase, "rest and digest."

Unlocking the wisdom of *rest and digest* reveals the ability to consciously recognize and understand how you react or respond to both positive and troubling experiences. Many people have no issue with positive experiences. Managing the troubling ones takes a little more work. You can do a better job of handling these challenging experiences by recognizing them when they occur and choosing a positive response rather than an unhelpful habitual reaction.

This is also true about how you process your life experiences through all five layers. Any discomfort you feel comes from what happened, when it happened, how it happened, or the emotional state you were left in when it ended. When you pay attention to how you process both food and life, you'll gain and deepen self-awareness and move "rest and digest" from words on a page to skillful action in your life. You can sharpen your ability to pay attention with the three techniques that follow.

It may be helpful to record the instructions into one of your devices for ease of practice.

Witnessing the Digestive System

INSTRUCTIONS

1. Bring yourself into a seated position with your spine comfortably straight.
2. Take a few slow deep breaths in and out through your nose.
3. Now visualize your breath as any color that speaks to you (white, blue, green, etc.).
4. Begin visualizing each inhalation flowing around and over your lips, tongue and teeth.
5. As you exhale, visualize your exhalation traveling to each part of your digestive system
6. Repeat this for three to five breaths, or longer if you are comfortable.
7. See your exhalation bring awareness, light and healing into each part of your digestive system as you move through the exercise.
8. Allow your exhalation to move downward into your stomach, liver, pancreas, your small intestine and your large intestine.

9. See your exhalation illuminate all of these places in your digestive system, like a flashlight shining into a cave.

10. As you look around, notice if there are places in your stomach, liver, pancreas, small intestine or large intestine that seem blocked, stuck, imbalanced, painful, tight or tense.

11. If you find such places, direct your exhalation, attention and awareness there.

12. See your breath as a flowing stream of light moving through your stomach, liver, pancreas, your small intestine and your large intestine, cleansing, clearing, healing, balancing and energizing all your digestive organs.

If practicing after a meal or before bedtime, try lying on your left side instead while doing this exercise. Some studies show that this position helps the digestive process, eases acid reflux and heartburn, and improves circulation in the intestines.

Seated Spinal Rotations

Next is a technique for occasional constipation, a condition you may experience when you're under stress or have overindulged in eating the wrong things. So if you are blocked up, backed up and miserable due to occasional constipation, pay attention.

Constipation is a perfect example of how the five layers of self-awareness interrelate with and affect each other. Here's how that might look.

- **Physical:** When you are constipated, your body is not operating optimally and can cause physical discomfort, which can affect your mood and relationships with others.

- **Energetic:** You may not be taking full deep breaths because of your discomfort. Energetically, constipation is considered a cold condition that requires heat to facilitate movement.

- **Mental:** You are probably miserable, feeling deep "down in the dumps" (pardon the pun) and feeling sorry for yourself.
- **Intuitive wisdom:** If it is awake and working, it will point out these interconnections, try to help you find a cause or source in one or more of your five layers, and perhaps suggest an action to help you address it.
- **Bliss:** The sweet relief of elimination.

If you find yourself dealing with occasional constipation, try this exercise and get in the groove for a smooth move.

You'll find this exercise enhances your digestive fire, the force at the source, by increasing heat and compression. This is because it massages the internal organs and increases peristaltic motion in the intestines.

Note: Seated spinal rotations are contraindicated for diarrhea, which is considered a hot condition.

INSTRUCTIONS

1. Sit in a comfortable position on the floor or in a chair with your spine aligned.
2. With your hands on your knees or thighs, begin rotating your torso in circles. You can imagine you are drawing circles on the ceiling with your upper body. Your circles can be small and tight or large and loose.
3. Let your breath come and go naturally. Pick a pace that feels comfortable, whether slow, medium or fast.

4. Continue for three minutes in one direction, then three minutes in the opposite direction. Setting a timer is helpful so you don't have to think about it.

5. Rest for a few breaths before getting up.

6. Repeat once or twice during the day, as needed.

I've been teaching this to my yoga students for years and, after trying it on their own, they say things like:

- "I was blocked for days. What a relief. Thank you!"
- "It really works."
- "Did you hear toilets flushing all over town after last night's class?" (This one is my favorite.)

Affirmation

I take in and take on only that which I can digest.

Affirmations set a positive intention for adopting a healthy lifestyle. They are one of many tools you can use to work with what you eat and what eats you.

This affirmation can be practiced with other techniques or as a separate standalone exercise. You can write it down on sticky notes and post them on your refrigerator, bathroom mirror, desk and dresser as a reminder of the intention you are focusing on. Regular and consistent use puts a focus on releasing negative emotions and managing stress. The goal is to improve your relationship with food, your digestive system, and your life experience.

HERE IS ONE LAST THING TO consider. Food isn't only an issue when there's too much of it. It's also a problem when there's not enough. If you donate to nonprofit organizations that work to reduce the suffering and inequities in the world, consider adding organizations like World Central Kitchen, Feeding America or a local nonprofit organization whose mission is to ensure that those less fortunate have enough to eat.

THE M-WORD

*There is no more creative force in the world
than the menopausal woman with zest.*

— Margaret Mead, cultural anthropologist

Sometimes referred to as the M-word, menopause is a change that
all biological women will experience, either naturally or surgi-
cally. "The Pause," as it is sometimes called, is the end of fertility and
the beginning of aging. It is also seen by the medical profession, Big
Pharma and many women as a condition to be medicated. Given
our modern healthcare and longer life spans, women in America
can anticipate spending close to one-third of their lives in a post-re-
productive state. That's a long time to see life through a glass darkly.
However, menopause has emerged from the shadows and is now
part of our cultural consciousness. It's time to enlighten up and
see menopause as a pause that refreshes.

Navigating our way through this sometimes difficult life change
can be challenging. The good news is that employing self-awareness skills and looking at our experience through the lens of the
five layers can help us see menopause as a personal laboratory for

finding individual approaches to address the changes our bodies experience during this transition.

There are several phases of menopause: premature menopause, premenopause, perimenopause and postmenopause, each with their own set of potential challenges. Of course, not every woman will experience all of them, but if you are in or approaching any one of them, it's important to recognize how stress may, or may not, impact you.

Here's one woman's story.

> P. is a yoga teacher and a friend. When we were sharing menopause stories, she told me she had a lot going on in her life in addition to menopause: a new husband, a twelve-year-old daughter from a former marriage, a late-life two-and-a-half-year-old baby girl from the new marriage, a stressful job as a researcher for a domestic violence project, a new yoga business, and a pending appearance as a witness in a sexual harassment lawsuit.
>
> Usually efficient and punctual, she was experiencing growing periods of mental fuzziness. In addition, she had been losing track of time, not showing up for some appointments and being late for others. She was experiencing what, for her, was an uncomfortable level of inner turmoil, but she recognized it was a process she'd need to acknowledge, address and work through.
>
> She has an interesting outlook on stress and menopause. She said, "I don't really think I have more stress than usual. It's just that I feel it more now."

And if you think that all challenges and symptoms disappear during postmenopause, think again. Hot flashes are one of the most common symptoms women experience.

My friend H. was no exception. She was surprised, appalled and pissed to be experiencing hot flashes a decade after her last period. When I told her it was normal, although understandably uncomfortable, she asked, "Why didn't my doctor ever tell me that?"

I'm guessing her doctor didn't know that, although hot flashes usually stop a year or two after menopause, some women will experience them for years.

In some societies where older women are honored and seen as wise, the menopausal transition is easier to navigate. In America, older is not better if you are a woman, at least not yet. Need an example? Google synonyms for menopause and you will find a long list of unflattering and unhelpful words and phrases. Here are a few.

- dried up
- wasted

- exhausted
- drained

- sterile
- ineffectual

Ugh! Give me a break!

Fortunately, movies, TV programs and magazines, along with drug and supplement ads, are beginning to present positive images of older women. But right now that adds only one drop of truth to an ocean of ignorance.

Here are two more drops of truth to consider... Although women are beginning to think of menopause as a time to address unfinished business and claim their power, many first need to deal with stressful challenges with their bodies.

While researching my master's thesis, titled "Menopause, Stress and Your Heart," I discovered a long list of challenging physical symptoms, including the most common:

- hot flashes and flushes
- night sweats
- weight gain

There are also two less common symptoms many women do not associate with menopause:

- formication (a feeling of ants crawling all over the body)
- frozen shoulder

Once while facilitating a menopause workshop at a local hospital, I mentioned those two uncommon symptoms. One woman literally jumped out of her chair and told me practically in tears that she was experiencing formication, had no idea it was related to menopause, thought she was going crazy, and had been ready to see a therapist. She thanked me, and I was grateful that a little of my knowledge had helped her.

That knowledge was hard-won. It came unexpectedly by way of an emergency hysterectomy. It started with my body and then reverberated through all five of my layers.

In my late 40s, it seemed like I had it all—professional success, a nice home, a blended family, and a busy social life. However, my second marriage had developed some serious problems. My job was financially rewarding but not fulfilling, and the social life that was glamorous and busy, turned repetitive, boring and empty. Restlessness, sadness and confusion filled my emotional space. What had gone wrong? These were things I had asked for, yet they were not making me happy. Everything in and around my life, my relationships, and my work became an effort. Frustration and stress grew and manifested in anxiety attacks, rashes, headaches, frequent sore throats, colds, bald spots and seasonal allergies.

My body was clearly sending signals I was not acknowledging or listening to. My life had come to a standstill, a holding pattern. There was no way back to a happy time, and I could not see a way to move forward. I was on a lateral drift, buffeted from side-to-side by a swelling tide of misery. And when it seemed like things could not get any worse, they did.

One day in March, my period was late. For a few days, I worried I might be pregnant. I was definitely not interested in becoming a mom again, especially with my life in a mess. Finally, my period came and dragged on for two weeks with cramping and flu-like symptoms. When my period stopped, my symptoms didn't. A few days later, intense abdominal pain woke me up in the middle of the night. I thought it was a bad case of constipation. My husband insisted on taking me to the emergency room. With great reluctance, I went. I did not want to bother anybody for what I thought was nothing. Three hours later, that nothing escalated into a CT scan, an ultrasound, an x-ray, and emergency exploratory surgery.

When I woke up, I learned I had undergone a complete abdominal hysterectomy, the result of ruptured ovarian abscesses. The doctor told me I was lucky to be alive. I spent two weeks in the hospital and six weeks at home recuperating. During my recovery, I felt debilitating weakness and general discomfort every day, slept for hours at a time, and felt disconnected from my lower body. My taste buds were off and the incision was tender and sore, but the worst sensations were the gas pains that began when my body started to wake up from the shock of surgery.

When I looked in the mirror, one very angry woman looked back at me. It was easy to read her mind. She was thinking, "Anger is not a good emotion." Good girls (and I was a good girl) don't get angry. They smile and reason their way out of difficult situations calmly and logically.

At that time, however, my anger was in full bloom. Unbeknownst to me, it had been there all along, damned up and held fast by the life I had chosen, the responsibilities I had accepted, and the expectations I was striving to meet. I went meno-postal! Anger, mood swings, irritability, crying jags and hot flashes kept coming. Then I ripped the phone off the wall and threw it into a corner. (Not my finest moment...) Even the dog stayed away from me.

As bad as I felt, I realized that if things were going to change, I needed to take action. I was slowly realizing that emotions are tools and the ability to acknowledge, feel and understand what they mean is a crucial step to healing. Eventually, that buried anger became the motivation to take action, which led to major changes in my life. Surgery and my sudden introduction to menopause had released the anger and guided me toward healing.

Being forced to give up doing, to experience being, was a struggle. During that scary and restless time, I often sat on the back deck. It had a peaceful view of a pond, a dense stand of trees, and a huge weeping cherry tree. One day in early May, its first tight pink bud appeared. I watched it with focus and fascination. Over the next few days, it magically bloomed. As it did, something inside me blossomed too. A full-blown insight emerged from deep inside, from my witness. I finally grasped I had almost died. I realized now that maybes and somedays could be snatched away and life could turn on a dime. The thought came to me, *There is another way to live, and I have got to find it.*

That thought kick-started my inner drive to tackle the unfinished business of my life. It was a major shift from the way I managed my life before the surgery. Moving quickly, making lists, adding more than could be done in a reasonable time, pushing the envelope, and running on stress and adrenaline to do just one more thing made me feel powerful, needed and in control.

Once I hit the pause button, I learned real change, deep life change, was something else and, although I did not know how to approach it or where it would take me, I knew I needed to do it. And it was going to take hard work as well as a lot of uncomfortable feelings and experiences.

I started with my body. I walked every day. It was hard, but I did it anyway. Two weeks passed before I could do a mile without resting. Yoga stretches were next. I have been practicing yoga since my son was six months old. At this writing, he's 52, so this has been a part of my life for decades now. I started slowly and gently. The movement, as always, felt good and was therapeutic. The resting was hard, but I did it anyway. I didn't have a choice. I was on leave from work and all social activities.

Years of trying to fix myself to fit into what I embraced as normal had not gotten me what I had been looking for. Now I did not want to fix myself; I wanted to understand myself, to go inside and go deep. I wanted to be alone to reflect and think.

I started to write. So I kept a journal and wrote short stories as well as a novel. The words poured out of me at a fast and furious rate. I talked to friends and began consciously unpacking emotional baggage. Some of that was revealed through my body as I did yoga or received regular massages. My hips and lower back released waves of sensation as I worked with the chronic contractions of my body. I'd heard my teachers describe this phenomenon, but if I hadn't had this experience, I would not have believed muscles and body structures could hold memories and emotions that can be released through movement and experienced through sensation.

As they say, "shift" happens. A major shift for me was the gradual change in my appearance. My Afro haircut brought me an incredible sense of freedom from my lifelong hair wars. Long skirts, boots and sweaters replaced business suits, pantyhose and high heels. What comfort! A sterling silver toe ring brought a delicious sense of artistic eccentricity as I embraced my creative side. All the external traditional and conservative trappings that helped me fit into a world in which I was no longer comfortable dropped away.

What people saw when they looked at the new me reflected who I had always been inside but had been too scared to reveal for fear of criticism, judgment and rejection. I was now out there and up-front with who I was inside. No more masks. Rejection came from some hurtful quarters, but now I was strong enough to see it for what it was. It had little or nothing to do with me and much more to do with the person criticizing, judging and rejecting.

Keeping a journal and writing were effective expressions of my journey as I sorted out new thoughts and feelings around the changes that were happening. The written word was more grounding than my thoughts, which seemed to flit and drift, like fireflies. Writing my thoughts, insights, memories and imaginings was like capturing those fireflies and putting them in a jar with a little grass so they could live and where I could pay attention and study them.

I also wrote a few poems, including this one about menopause.

> **my menopause poem**
> Listen to the hipbones
> my hipbones held me up
> carried me forward
> through bubbling joy
> carried me forward
> through secret rage
> carried me forward
> to now
> me, the lucky one
> me, the plucky one
> firstborn
> compulsive
> golden
>
> my hipbones insulated me
> rushing past skepticism
> moving beyond obstacles
> knocking down barriers
> these bones guarded my heart
> brushing right by
> careless slips of the tongue

these bones
protected me from others
protected me from myself

now at midlife
my hipbones rebel
joints lose juice
muscles freeze
forward motion halts
pain is constant
bone rubs bone
sparks fly
doubt and confusion
catch fire
their questions
burn my soul
how do I live without moving on
where would I go if I could

my hipbones refuse
a future of onward
a future of upward
they whisper
then speak
then shout
I still myself to listen
and hear the answer
my next move forward
will be within

My acceptance of the real meaning and gift of menopause has evolved slowly. The hard work has been worth it. My experience taught me this time of life could be an amazing and ongoing journey in which acknowledgment, self-awareness and healing can happen.

Practice: Know Your Menopause

Quality to Embody: Acknowledgment

THE WAY YOU MOVED, ARE MOVING, or will move through menopause can transform your inner and outer experience. The first step
is to acknowledge it as an opportunity to make peace with your
body and the past before you make plans for the future.

My path forward included designing a small research project and
earning a master's degree in yoga therapy and mind/body health
based on my hypothesis that most women deal with menopause in
one of three ways.

1. Fix it and forget it.
2. Just hang in there until it's over.
3. Deepen self-awareness and navigate life with clarity, contentment and resilience.

In other words, they choose to forget it, process it or transform it.

Fix It and Forget It

The "fix it and forget it" response can mean different things to
different women. Some seek medication or lifestyle fixes for their
physical symptoms and go no further. Others may suffer no physical
symptoms and simply choose to forget menopause even happened.

Several menopausal and postmenopausal women I talked with
for my thesis fell into this category. Their responses ranged from
fixing symptoms, like hot flashes, with hormones or natural supplements to expressing relief that menopause had come and gone
and they were getting on with their lives. Here are a few comments.

- "It means freedom from the inconveniences of having
  a period."
- "I'm afraid it didn't mean a great deal to me."
- "Really have not given menopause much thought."

If you are dealing with symptom management, here is a "fix it" technique for one of the most common issues, hot flashes. It can be done anytime, anywhere, and has helped several of my yoga students and a few others, including my flashing friend, H., and my sister-in-law. Neither practices yoga, nor are they interested in starting.

Cooling Breath for Hot Flashes

This breathing exercise often stops a hot flash if caught when it begins. Practice the Cooling Breath consistently so it will be readily available when you feel a flash or a flush coming on.

INSTRUCTIONS

1. Sit (or stand) with a comfortably aligned spine.
2. Purse your lips like you were going to whistle.
3. Slowly draw air over the tongue and deep into the lungs.
4. Close your mouth and exhale slowly through your nose.
5. Repeat as many times as you like and as often as needed.

You can also practice the Cooling Breath in bed if you have hot flashes during the night.

Process It

Managing menopause often involves much more than fixing physiological changes in the body. The process of reflection leads to discovering opportunities for conscious self-healing and change. Like a caterpillar, you may want to wrap yourself in a cocoon, check out, and let something more powerful than yourself take over.

Others who fit the "process it" response said:

- "It's a change in my life, an aging process, but one I want to control."
- "I feel like I have been transitioning for the last fourteen years. I'm thinking menopause is a process, not an event."

- "I know I'm going to experience many changes, and I want to learn more about how to handle them so I don't feel so frustrated."

Many women who see menopause as a process first embark on a journey of external self-improvement. This may mean enrolling in a weight loss program, joining a gym, or even changing a hairstyle, diet, clothes, job or relationship. Even positive changes can be stressful but finding ways to manage stress can ease the process.

Here is a stress reduction technique I've been using for over fifteen years. Legs-up-the-Chair Pose helps to calm the nervous system and relax the body.

Legs-up-the-Chair Pose

1. Lie on the floor with your legs on a chair so your calves are at a 90-degree angle to your thighs.
2. Place a pillow under your head for comfort if you like.
3. Relax in this position for five to ten minutes. (Use music and a timer if you like.)
4. To come out, keep your head on the floor as you inhale and raise your arms over your head.
5. As you exhale, place your hands below the knees (or behind the thighs) and pull both knees toward your chest. Alternatively, you can separate them, pressing the right knee toward your right armpit and the left knee toward your left armpit.
6. Hold your position for about twenty seconds.
7. Roll to one side and slowly bring yourself into a seated position.

If getting down and back up from the floor doesn't work for you, you can do this in bed with your legs on a stack of pillows.

Transform It

Letting go for a caterpillar results in a metaphorical death as it transforms into a butterfly. As you let go of illusions that keep you from examining your deepest life dreams and your demons, you are able to transform and see yourself in a new light, as a complete being worthy of existence.

The women who saw this time of life as an opportunity for transformation said:

- "I guess you could say menopause launched me into my search for myself because that's when I started all my work on me and began handling my interpersonal as well as physical problems."
- "Spiritually, I feel as though I'm free at last to pursue my own preferences in life."
- "Menopause is a time to evaluate one's life and chart a deliberate path of growth for the next phase of life."

Christiane Northrup, MD, says:

> *As a woman makes the transition to the second half of her life, she finds herself in a struggle not only with her own aversion to conflict and confrontation, but also with the culture's view of how women "should" be. The body's inner wisdom gets its last best chance of breaking through culturally erected barriers, while shining a light on aspects of a woman's life that need work.*[12]

Northrup attributes much of this internal push to actual changes in the brain's temporal lobes caused by hormonal shifts.

---

12 Christiane Northrup, MD. *The Wisdom of Menopause: Creating Physical and Emotional Health and Healing During the Change.* Bantom Books, New York, 2001.

It's wake-up call and women who are ready to answer can find helpful advice from those who have written extensively about menopause and ways to view life postmenopause as a transformative experience. Here are four that continue to help me on my path of transformation.

- *The Wisdom of Menopause: Creating Physical and Emotional Health and Healing During the Change* by Christiane Northrup, MD
- *Transformation Through Menopause* by Marian Van Eyk McCain
- *The Third Chapter: Passion, Risk and Adventure in the 25 Years After 50* by Sara Lawrence-Lightfoot
- *The Second Half of Life: Opening the Eight Gates of Wisdom* by Angeles Arrien

Your menopause is personal and, like a fingerprint, it is uniquely yours. Given today's emphasis on health and longevity, it makes sense to take this time to enlighten up and consciously decide how you want to experience (or are experiencing) this stage of life.

Your Second Layer of Self-Awareness: Energetic

The Taittiriya Upanishad depicts breath and energy (the second layer of self-awareness) as being integrated and inseparable even though we separate them to define, discuss, explain and explore them. B. K. S. Iyengar says, "Energy and awareness (both cosmic entities) act as friends. Where one goes, the other follows."[13]

The oxygen we breathe nourishes our body and brain and sustains life. Like our body, oxygen is material and can be weighed and measured. Our energy is immaterial and is the invisible life force that animates us at all levels. It enters our body with each breath and gives us the power to think, create, move, work, live and love. Energy flows to, from and through the body interpenetrating our physical systems. While some of this energy can be scientifically measured, other aspects remain in the subtle realm.

---

13   B. K. S. Iyengar. *Light on Life: The Yoga Journey to Wholeness, Inner Peace, and Ultimate Freedom*. Rodale Books. Kindle edition.

Breath and Breathing

BREATH IS THE ASPECT OF THIS layer that is, perhaps, the most "real," meaning it is firmly rooted in the material world discernible with the five senses. Most of us are familiar with the major parts of our respiratory system; nose and nasal cavity, mouth, throat, trachea, lungs and the muscles of respiration. We've seen pictures and diagrams in our anatomy books, and we understand that they can be dissected and studied after death.

Scientific research and integrative health professionals support the idea that the proper flow of oxygen is necessary to maintain optimal physical health in all of our body systems and affects sleep, memory, energy levels and mental focus.

Fortunately, we don't have to think about each inhale and exhale we make. Our autonomic nervous system handles that function. It's automatic and involuntary. However, with awareness and practice, we can learn to consciously control and vary our breathing to change our physical, energetic and mental states in several ways. We can learn to:

- energize and warm the body.
- relax and calm ourselves when feeling tense.
- manage our stress levels.
- focus the mind.

Our lungs can hold six liters of air, which equals approximately one and a half gallons. Sadly, most of us do not use the full capacity of our lungs. Breathing fully and efficiently begins when we inhale. Breathing through the nose both warms and cleans the air before it reaches the lungs. The air then travels down the back of the throat into the windpipe and through the bronchial tubes, which carry the air through the lungs and into smaller air passages called "bronchioles." The bronchioles end in tiny balloon-like air sacs called "alveoli." We have over 300 million alveoli that are surrounded by tiny blood vessels called "capillaries." This proximity enables oxygen to pass through the alveoli walls and into the blood.

The oxygenated blood is carried to the heart, which pumps it through the body to provide oxygen to the cells, tissues, organs and brain. The body then releases carbon dioxide, which the blood carries back to the lungs, where it is released when we exhale. An interesting fact is that the brain is only 2 percent of the body's weight, yet it needs 20 percent of the body's available oxygen; so the practice of deep breathing and fully oxygenating the blood is important to our overall well-being.

Research says when our blood is fully oxygenated, our cells are rejuvenated every night as we sleep. Optimum oxygen levels give us:

- more energy.
- enhanced brain function.
- lower stress.
- less fatigue.

Lack of oxygen weakens every body system and is a key factor in many diseases. For example, a weakened immune system can lead to viral infections, inflammation, heart disease and premature aging.

How do we know improving awareness of the breath and our breathing process works? Here's one inspiring example.

Richard Brown and Patricia Gerbarg, both MDs, have been using simple breathing techniques to work with survivors of disasters, such as the World Trade Center attacks, the earthquake in Haiti, the Gulf of Mexico oil spill, and the wars in South Sudan and Rwanda. Their work provides easily accessible solutions to stress-related issues like anxiety, depression, insomnia and trauma. It's interesting to note that most of the individuals who were helped by their techniques did not have a consistent yoga or meditation practice. Their work is impressive and firmly based on scientific research.[14]

Becoming aware of our breathing and learning to breathe deeply and efficiently is one of the most important practices we can incorporate into our daily lives for optimal health. When we do point the light of self-awareness toward our breath, we begin to develop an awareness of the other aspect of this layer of being—our energy.

Energy

THIS ASPECT OF OUR SECOND LAYER of self-awareness is a bit more mysterious. Energy is said to surround, penetrate and expand beyond our physical body and interrelate with everything in our environment. It is known by many names.

- *Prana* in India
- *Chi* (or *Qi*) in China
- *Ki* in Japan
- *Mana* in Polynesia
- *Orgone, bioplasma* and *animal magnetism* by early researchers and practitioners in the United States
- *Energy fields* and *life force* by modern researchers and practitioners worldwide

Some useful analogies have been developed to explain how the process of breathing is connected to energy and the larger world. The analogy that describes this most clearly is the relationship between humans and trees. With our internal lungs, we breathe in oxygen and exhale carbon dioxide. Trees, through their external lungs (the leaves), breathe in carbon dioxide and exhale oxygen. With each inhale, we take in the energy of oxygen molecules from

---

14   Richard P. Brown, MD, and Patricia L. Gerbarg, MD. *The Healing Power of the Breath.* Shambhala Publications, Boston, MA, 2012.

the trees to animate, feed and nourish our body. With each exhale, we send the energy of carbon dioxide molecules to animate, feed and nourish the trees.

Science acknowledges human energy fields exist and identifies those that can be measured; the electromagnetic and biomagnetic fields generated by all living cells, tissues, organs and the body as a whole. Electrical brain activity can be measured with an electro-encephalogram (also known as an EEG) and heart activity with an electrocardiograph (also known as an ECG or, more commonly, as an EKG).

More subtle energy fields exist, but scientists are not in agreement on what they are or how to measure them. Theoretical physicists believe these energy fields hold our atoms together and their vibrations allow us to function in our seemingly solid material world.

Eastern healthcare practitioners and philosophers consider these subtle energy fields to be a complex and yet unexplored area that impacts breath, the act of breathing, our overall health, and our relationship to our environment. We can sense it, feel it, and some people can see it, but as yet it has not been weighed or measured by scientific instruments.

The presence, activity and relevance of subtle energy fields to our existence, health and well-being is not a new idea to students of ancient wisdom traditions, but they are only beginning to be explored by modern science. Here are three quotes that illustrate this.

The first is from the Isha Upanishad.

> *The Self is everywhere. Bright is the Self,*
> *Indivisible, untouched by sin, wise,*
> *Immanent and transcendent. He it is*
> *Who holds the cosmos together.*

— *The Upanishads*, translation by
Eknath Easwaran

The next is from Nikola Tesla, a 19th-century engineer and scientist.

> *If you want to find the secrets of the universe, think in terms of energy, frequency and vibration.*

The last is from Albert Einstein, the legendary theoretical physicist.

> *Energy cannot be created or destroyed, it can only be changed from one form to another.*

While Western science tackles energy in all of its measurable forms, Eastern wisdom traditions provide self-awareness explorers with ways to grasp, understand and work with our subtle energy. Prana is said to enter the body with the breath and move around the body through energy channels analogous to blood vessels. The Chinese call these channels *meridians.* That's where the needles are inserted during an acupuncture session. Yogis call them *nadis.* They form our energy anatomy, which exists alongside of and penetrates our physical anatomy.

It is this energy that connects everything and everybody. How we understand and relate to that basic truth can have a transformative effect on how we live and interact with others and with our environment.

Here's another way to think about energy. You walk into a room and pick up an uncomfortable vibe, a friend tells you that you have "good energy," or you are buying a car and have narrowed your options to two. One is economically sound, but you buy the other one because you are drawn to it and it just "feels" right.

Direct experience of the energy aspect of this layer of self-awareness remains in the subtle realm for most of us until practice or grace renders it noticeable. This may be because most of us can't see energy, but with practice and awareness, we can learn to detect it by tuning in to the following:

- Times of the day when we feel tired, spacey or energized.
- Sensations like tingling and pulsing, warmth or coolness, heaviness or lightness.
- Feeling balanced, calm or contented.

We can learn to detect imbalances in our energy through our breathing patterns, aches, pains, poor digestion, lack of motivation, or feeling over-stressed, exhausted or fatigued.

In this world of faster is better and "TMI" (too much information), many of us spend hours dissipating our energy without taking time to recharge our batteries. As a result, we seek external ways to charge ourselves through energy drinks or supplements.

Whether we boost ourselves externally or find natural ways to manage our energy, understanding its role in our life is important. It takes time and more than a little awareness. Energy is a factor in every facet of the human condition: physical, mental, emotional and spiritual. We all have the ability to work with our energy and use it to change how we perceive our issues, actions, behavior and ultimately ourselves.

When we detect an imbalance, we can make an effort to address it or do what we can to change it, manage it, or accept it. For example, sometimes we need to transform our energy to light our fire and give ourselves a boost. According to the Mayo Clinic, nearly everyone is overtired or overworked from time to time.

Temporary fatigue or lack of energy usually has an identifiable cause, such as long to-do lists, lack of sleep, feeling blue, sad and down in the dumps, or overeating carbohydrates. Unrelenting fatigue is a whole different matter. When fatigue lasts longer than usual, is more profound, and isn't relieved by rest, it's a sure sign you need to see a medical professional.

On the other end of the energy spectrum, we may need to transform our energy to slow the burn. This burn state may manifest imbalance in one of two ways:

- We feel nervous or anxious and have difficulty sleeping, feel "spacey" or unfocused, and have poor digestion.
- Our mind works overtime with a burning need for perfection, competition and overachievement, which can lead to feeling irritable, provoked and angry.

To begin work with this layer, we'll employ the second step of the Nine Steps to Self-Awareness.

Step 2. Become Aware of Your Breath and Energy States

Instructions

1. Become aware of your breathing.

   - Integrate the process of breathing into your conscious awareness.
   - Check in regularly to become aware of the flow of your breath.
   - Pay attention to where in your body you feel your breath moving.
   - Understand how you breathe when you are relaxed, energized or calm.
   - Be able to describe how your breath feels when you are anxious, angry, scared or stressed.
   - Use effective breathing to improve your moods and physical health.

2. Use your breath to change and balance your energy states.

- Light your fire by creating energy when feeling tired or drained.
- Slow the burn by reducing excess energy when feeling wired and overwhelmed.
- Notice, balance and manage your physical and mental states.

3. Become aware of the movement of energy within and around you.

- Notice any tingling or pulsing, absence or presence of sensations (flowing, stuckness, emptiness, heaviness or lightness), or differences in temperature (like areas of coolness or heat in the body).
- Evaluate whether your daily energy fluctuations have a consistent pattern.
- Remember to check in on your energy state during pleasurable and stressful situations.

The chapters that follow in this section focus on understanding breath and energy, building strong connections between body and mind, and developing awareness of the importance of managing the energy of communication and behavior.

The tips and techniques at the end of each chapter provide "how to do it" suggestions for enhancing the ability to practice commitment, connection, reflection and discipline. As you read them, remember that breath and energy are inseparable and interchangeable. When you see the word "breath" used, energy is automatically implied and vice versa.

$E=MC^2$

All energy is only borrowed,
and one day you have to give it back.

— Neytiri in *Avatar*

This line will stay in my mind for as long as I live. The math and science behind it, with its theories of how energy manifests in the universe, make my eyes gloss over, but thinking about energy from the philosophical perspective helps me understand myself.

For health and peace of mind, we all need to be aware of how our energy fluctuates during any given day, week, month, year and stage of life, and how it impacts what we think, feel and believe until the day comes when we have to give it back.

Here's how science and philosophy think about energy.
Scientific theories say:

- All matter we see, hear, smell, taste and touch is made of vibrating strings of energy and space.
- The laws of energy are not the same for the things we can see (ourselves and the material world) and the "spooky" action of

things we cannot see or fully understand (such as subatomic particles, dark matter and dark energy).

Philosophy says:

- We are spiritual beings having a physical experience.
- Experiencing everyday life is heightened and enlightened when we understand that energy exists in, around and through our physical bodies.

So, what does that have to do with $E=mc^2$? You probably recognize this formula from Albert Einstein's equation of the Theory of Relativity. One of the major principles of this theory describes the relationship between energy (E), mass (m) and (c^2) the speed of light, squared.

This chapter looks at Einstein's equation through a philosophical lens and nudges it from the scientific realm toward the mystical, and from an expression of the external world to a deeper understanding of the internal world. We can use it as a tool to help us enlighten up. From this perspective, $E=mc^2$ looks like this.

E = Energy is needed to choose change and make a commitment to take action. To enlighten up, we will need to use physical, mental, emotional, psychological and spiritual energy. Energy flows where intention goes.

m = Mass is you, me and the world we all share: our bodies, homes, communities, the planet and everything we engage with our senses of sight, hearing, taste, touch and smell.

c^2 = Consciousness squared represents the two levels needed for the enlightening up process.

The first level of consciousness (c^1) is awareness of any uncomfortable symptom, issue or situation that calls for change or healing and that we can sense with our everyday thinking mind. For example, if you eat too much fried food and get a stomachache, you notice that, take a little something, get out your heating pad, and wait until it passes (or until you pass it). Done. Gone.

However, if a symptom, issue or situation is chronic, has a pattern, and is noticeably affecting your life, it needs additional energy and attention. The second level of consciousness (c^2) is the search for the source of an unhelpful thought, emotion or belief that may be feeding what you are facing. For example, if you consistently experience issues with your digestion, you may be able to trace it to an overall change in your digestive system due to age, an unhelpful reaction to stress, or a message from your unconscious urging you to make a major change in work, relationships or creativity. Once that is traced and made conscious, you can decide what, if anything, to do about it.

Here's a personal example to illustrate this process. The first level of consciousness occurred for me when I noticed pain in my lower back and right hip tended to flare up when I was feeling stressed. I faced it by taking ibuprofen and using some creative energy to write a poem.

Oh, my aching back
I hate the friggin' pain
But if I take a mindful look
What wisdom could I gain?

My next question was: Why is stress affecting my lower back and hip? Why didn't it hit me with headaches, panic attacks or high blood pressure? Being curious and wanting to know the why of most everything, I looked into the causes of back pain.

Back pain cause number one: Mechanical, physical or traumatic injury caused by poor posture; sitting, standing or walking improperly; carrying heavy, uneven weights and not carrying them properly; doing exercise not suited for one's level of fitness. There are also medical conditions or diseases, such as herniated discs, scoliosis, arthritis and osteoporosis. And of course, there are accidents and injuries. All of these can drain your energy.

Over the next several months I made appointments with a chiropractor, a massage therapist, an acupuncturist, a reflexologist and a sports medicine doctor. All I got in return was temporary relief, a smaller bank balance, and no answers. That is, until I saw an integrative positional therapist, who gave me a physical reason for the pain in short order. He informed me my pelvis was chronically misaligned in three ways: 1) it is rotated, 2) one hip is functionally higher than the other and, 3) I have a deep lumbar curve. (*Great!* I thought sarcastically).

Then on the recommendation of a friend, I made an appointment with an orthopedic surgeon, who took an x-ray and gave me another diagnosis. He told me I had developed *spondylolisthesis*, a condition in which one of the spinal vertebrae slips out of place onto the vertebra below it, often pressing on a nerve and causing localized and referred pain.

Mine, according to the doctor, was likely caused by an old trauma or accident. *Aha!* I flashed back to 1992 about four weeks post-op from my total hysterectomy. I had gone out to get the mail and, on the way back to the house, I slipped and fell hard, right on my butt. Okay, the first two questions answered. I had a misaligned pelvis and a problem in my lumbar spine making that spot a handy target for stress to manifest physically and get my attention.

The exercises and nutritional supplements I received helped. The pain is chronic, but when it flares up and intensifies, I know what to do to reduce it.

Back pain cause number two: Emotional and psychological. According to many alternative and complementary health practitioners, emotional difficulties, mental concerns and stress often manifest in the back. Did I have emotional difficulties or mental concerns? That would be a definite yes. I recognized I was anxious, irritable, stressed out, and unhappy with my job, my marriage and the length of my self-imposed to-do lists. Did this affect my energy levels, causing me to feel drained and tired? That would be another definite yes.

I needed answers to the energetic connection between my emotional issues and my lower back and hip pain. The second level of consciousness kicked in when I decided to trace my stress mess to its source. If I could do that, I'd be able to figure out what, if anything, I could do to manage the stress and pain, so it would no longer manage me.

I committed my energy to the process and slowly began to recognize that stress, irritation and pain flared up when I was in situations that left me feeling stuck, blocked or trapped. The situation could be as simple as waiting in a long line at the supermarket or sitting in stalled traffic, or as complicated as navigating a difficult social or relationship situation.

Going more deeply, I recognized my reaction was layered and under the stress, irritation and pain was a layer of, wait for it, fear. *Aha!* Now I was getting somewhere. What was I afraid of? Slowly it dawned on me that fear popped up when I felt powerless and not in control of a situation. That was a wake-up call.

Feeling stuck, blocked or trapped is an energy-draining situation. My c^1 mind knows I always have a choice to regain a sense of control. I can change lines at the supermarket, take an alternate route in traffic, and use assertive communication skills to change or leave an uncomfortable social or relationship situation. Those are rational courses of action. Even though they are available to me, why didn't I exercise them? It was time for a deeper dive into c^2 consciousness.

Could I unearth an unhelpful thought, emotion or belief that was feeding the fear and keeping me stuck, blocked and trapped? Yes, I could. I finally traced it back to a fear of calling attention to myself, embarrassing myself in public, being rude, or making a scene. I recognized that as a lamentable hangover from my good girl training as a Black woman raised to be a "credit to the race."

Now that I understood the energetic connection between feeling stuck, my physical pain, and its emotional source, I needed to make a change. Instead of a fear-based, stressful reaction, I could make one of three choices: change the situation, change myself, or leave.

In a long line of traffic, I change lanes, take an alternate route, or do slow, deep breathing to reduce my irritation. Will the world end if I have to wait a few minutes before moving on to the next task on my to-do list? No, it will not. And do I really need to control difficult social and relationship situations? Again, no. I relax into them, breathe deeply, and go with the flow. And if that doesn't work, I find the most graceful way to exit.

Here's a summary of the $E=mc^2$ process through my first four layers.

- **Physical:** Became aware of back and hip pain.
- **Energetic:** Noticed how it affected my energy levels.
- **Mental (c^1):** Developed an awareness of mental-emotional reactions to pain and stress.
- **Intuitive wisdom (c^2):** Traced my issue to its sources: fear, an unhelpful need to control, and "good girl" messages about how I needed to be.

This type of personal work means you consciously learn to recognize difficult situations and find ways to change them, deal with them, or avoid them to live with more clarity, contentment and resilience.

Practice: Solve Your Energy Equation

Quality to Embody: Commitment

IT TAKES COMMITMENT TO RECOGNIZE AND work with the second layer of self-awareness. Here are three exercises you can use to light your fire, slow your burn, or balance your energy, depending on what you most need right now.

Breath of Joy

To light your fire, think: move, stimulate and energize.

This lack of energy state typically hits after an extended period of long to-do lists; lack of sleep; feeling blue, sad and down in the dumps; or overeating carbohydrates—you know, bread, pasta, potato chips and sugar—the ultimate comfort foods.

If you are experiencing unrelenting fatigue, please seek professional help.

For occasional fatigue, try the Breath of Joy. You can do this standing up or sitting in a chair. The Breath of Joy energizes the whole body, increases oxygen levels in the bloodstream, and helps to focus the mind.

Note: This practice may not be appropriate for those with high blood pressure or who have eye or head injuries.

INSTRUCTIONS

1. Stand or sit with your feet shoulder-width apart. If standing, allow the knees to bend slightly.

2. Inhale one-third of your lung capacity as you swing your arms forward, bringing them parallel to each other at shoulder level, with palms facing the ceiling

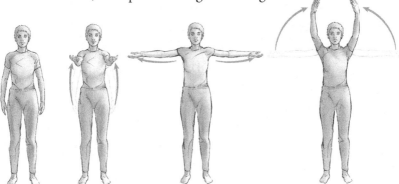

3. Continue inhaling to two-thirds capacity and stretch your arms out to the side to shoulder level, like wings.

4. Inhale to full capacity and swing your arms forward, bringing them up over your head.

5. Open your mouth and exhale with a "ha" as you bend forward and down toward the floor.

6. If you are standing, bend your knees more deeply as you sink into a standing squat and swing your arms down and behind you, like a diver. If you're seated in a chair, bend forward and swing your arms down and behind your body.

Repeat this technique up to nine times. Don't force or strain the body or breath; simply be absorbed by the peacefully stimulating rhythm. When you feel complete, close your eyes and experience the energetic effects. Notice if your heart is beating faster. Feel any pulsing sensations in your face and arms or tingling in the palms of your hands.

Two-to-One Breathing

If you feel nervous or anxious, have difficulty sleeping, feel unfocused, your mind may be working overtime. You may be feeling a burning need for perfection, competition and overachievement that leads to feelings of irritation, frustration and anger. In other words, you may need to slow the burn, so think: cool, calm and relax.

Here's an exercise you may find helpful to reduce an energy excess. Two-to-One Breathing slows the breath, lengthens the exhalation, calms the nervous system, and induces relaxation. Better yet, it can be done anytime, anywhere.

INSTRUCTIONS

1. Bring yourself to a comfortable seated position.
2. Now notice how long it takes you to inhale. (For example, 1, 2, 3, 4 counts or more.)
3. Over several breathing cycles, consciously allow your exhalation to grow up to twice as long as your inhalation. (For example, 2, 4, 6, 8 counts or more.)
4. Continue for two to three minutes, or for as long as you are comfortable.

Balance Your Energy

When your energy is harmonized, you are more likely to find yourself feeling stable, grounded and balanced between alertness and relaxation.

Try using the Gesture of the Mountain to balance your energy. It is also known as "Hakini mudra" in the yoga tradition.

INSTRUCTIONS

1. Hold your hands in front of your body.
2. Touch the tips of your fingers and thumb on one hand to the tips of the fingers and thumb on your other hand.
3. Allow space between the palms as though you were holding a tennis ball.
4. Relax your shoulders.
5. Rest your hands in your lap.
6. Breathe normally, while holding the Gesture of the Mountain for two to

three minutes, or longer if you feel comfortable.

How do we know when our energy is moving toward a balanced state? It's when:

- we move with lightness, balance, grace and ease.
- we are creative and spontaneous.
- sleep comes easily and digestion is good.
- we feel competent and in charge, able to accomplish what we set out to do, and comfortable about expressing ourselves in the world.
- we feel stable, grounded, calm, safe and connected to the physical world, our families, friends and support communities.

BUILDING BRIDGES

Voyager, there are no bridges,
one builds them as one walks.

— Gloria Anzaldúa

The idea for this chapter evolved from a conversation I had with my good friend M. I was talking to her about the importance of paying attention to the messages your body, breath, energy and mind send so you can make more productive decisions about living healthier. She understood what to do but wanted to know how to do it. I promised I'd work on some specific ideas to share with her.

I needed an analogy that could paint a clear picture of what can seem like a complicated process. I found it in the quote above from Gloria Anzaldúa. It had been staring me in the face for years every time I opened my refrigerator. I first read it on a calendar of inspirational daily quotes, printed on the December 28th page. It spoke to me, so I ripped it out and stuck it on my refrigerator. It has been with me through four refrigerators and three moves.

Does it have significance to the question my friend posed? I think so. Building bridges between our layers is a great way to pay attention to the messages going back and forth between them. Building, repairing, maintaining and occasionally upgrading the bridges can increase positive connections between our thoughts and behavior. And building bridges, physical or mental, takes energy—a lot of energy—specifically conscious and concentrated energy.

I knew from my studies, the mind speaks with thoughts and emotions, while the body, breath and energy speak with sensation. These are very different modes of communication. When the bridges between them are in good repair with wide, clearly marked lanes, our whole being is in alignment. If one or more of the bridges is damaged or in need of repair, the messages that go back and forth are mixed. It can be tricky to figure out which ones to listen to. The mind can often be a bullshit artist, trying to fake us out and pretend everything is okay. It is often our breath and body that tell us the truth if we stop, listen and make the connections.

Here are a few real-life examples I planned to share with M.

Recently, I agreed to go on a bus trip to a nearby tourist attraction with a friend. To make our connections easier, I invited her to spend the night at my place, then carpool to the bus pickup site.

To get ready for her arrival, I pulled out the futon in my office/guest room, made it up, and set out a washcloth and towels. I like order, so I planned to put the futon back and neaten the room immediately after she left. I didn't. For some reason, I couldn't. For the next few days, my mind said, "I need to put the futon back," but the message didn't seem to be able to cross the bridge from mind to body, and the energy to do it was simply and uncharacteristically not there.

Finally, ten days later, with my mind insisting, I marched into the guest room, ready to check this task off my to-do list. Looking at the futon in bed format, the urge to keep it that way and re-organize the room seized hold. That was totally unexpected. I had planned to reset the futon, go grocery shopping, and then cook.

Instead, my mind, breath and body aligned with the energy to rearrange the room.

I could see it in my mind. My body was energized. My breath calmed. With quick, efficient movements, I stripped the furniture of books, laptop, office supplies and files. Then I re-arranged the room, moving the furniture around. When I finished, I was energized, content and satisfied.

It is marvelous when your whole being is in joyful, balanced agreement. But when it is not, there can be a disconnect between mind, body and breath. The results can be surprising and powerful.

Many years ago, my nine-year-old stepson was enrolled in a summer enrichment camp at the university where I worked. One afternoon at 3:45, he bounded into my office to wait for his father who was scheduled to pick him up at 4 p.m. At 3:50 p.m., his father called to say he was delayed at work and wouldn't be able to come. I called his mother. She wasn't able to pick him up either.

I was scheduled to chair a professional meeting off-campus at 4:30 p.m. I was stuck, frustrated and angry. At 4:15 p.m., I drove to the meeting with my stepson in the car. I kept a careful lid on my anger since I did not want him to know what I was feeling. Getting him upset would not help.

I pulled up to a stop sign and waited to make a left turn. In a nanosecond, my anger went systemwide. Energetically, it felt like a volcano spewing red-hot lava from my belly up to my head. My breath was shallow and stuck in my throat. I felt heavy, tight and constricted. Mentally, of course, I was seething.

What was curious is that suddenly I was consciously aware of all of it. Body, breath and mind feeling the same emotion at the same time but expressing it differently. It was like being in the eye of a hurricane. Some small part of me was calm and observant, noticing the whirling anger in my mind, the constriction of breath in my chest, and feeling the volcano erupt in my body before finally quieting. Once I arrived at the meeting, I gave my stepson a book and successfully ran the meeting. The whole experience was amazing.

Sometimes, mixed messages cross the bridge between body and mind, and it can be tricky to know which one to listen to. When that happens and if we're in "aware mode," we can focus our energy and figure out the next best move.

For example, I start most days with a mental or written to-do list. (My yoga practice is not on the list because that is part of my daily routine, like eating breakfast and brushing my teeth.) The purpose of the list is to check off every item before the evening arrives.

One morning, I had five items on my list.

1. Exercise class
2. Make a deposit at the bank
3. Pick up new sunglasses
4. Buy sheets and a non-stick sauté pan
5. Stop at Trader Joe's for groceries

After items one and two were checked off, I picked up the sunglasses and was on the way to cross number four off my list when my body sent a message that lunchtime had come and gone and it wanted food. I listened and drove to a nearby restaurant for a small salad and half a sandwich. While I ate, my mind was busy planning the most efficient way to complete the last two items on my list. My body was sending signals it wanted to head home and rest. My mind wanted to finish the list and was thinking it could dig deep, pull the energy needed from the body, and push through to the goal of "done."

My body simply refused to get up from the chair. How interesting. My mind said, "Get up and go," but my body, breath and energy replied, "No! Rest and digest." So I sat and waited for an answer. I did not want to call attention to myself, so I kept my eyes open, looked out the window, and focused my gaze on a tree. After a few minutes of stillness, my mind capitulated, and I headed home.

Sometimes the bridges are in such poor condition that unconscious thinking and behavior overwhelm all connections between them. When that happens, a large sign gets posted across the entrance: **Bridge Closed For Repair, Do Not Cross.**

My friend B. and I used to spend way too much time bashing men. Talk about a bridge over troubled waters! Both of us had been through unhappy relationships, ending in breakups or divorce. We had plenty of vitriol, negativity and condemnations to share. This all happened in the heat of the early women's movement. We were beginning to examine anything and everything in our lives we had taken for granted or accepted as the way things were and would always be.

One day, I was complaining to her about a first date gone wrong. I'd known the guy as a friend for years. We were exploring the idea of taking the friendship up a notch. I liked and respected him. I'd talked him through a couple of his failed relationships, and he through a couple of mine. We were taking it slow because moving from friendship to romance can ruin a friendship. That first date nixed the romance and very nearly tanked the friendship. He walked me to my apartment and, as we were saying goodnight at the door, I noticed he had a button missing on his jacket. He told me he'd had it in his pocket for a while but lost it somewhere.

Being ever helpful, I suggested he take the extra button from inside the left lapel and use it to replace the missing one. Then it happened. He smiled and asked me to do it for him. Uh-oh! There it was. Him, Tarzan; me, Jane. The scene played out in my mind. First, a button that needs sewing; then a shirt that needs ironing or an apartment that needs cleaning. I felt misunderstood and taken for granted much as I had in my marriage. I thought I had divorced that feeling along with my husband, but here it was, staring at me through new eyes. I had just won a hard-fought battle for independence, empowerment and a measure of authenticity and was not happy with the prospect of having him, especially him, expect me to play the traditional female role. Maybe later, after we'd tested the relationship a bit more, I would have been happy to sew that button on, but I wasn't ready. I didn't want to repeat past patterns. My divorce, and the pain that went along with it, was too new. I was pissed.

I was in the middle of relating this to B., body tensed, eyes squinted, lips twisted, mind disconnected, when all of a sudden, I saw and heard myself mid-rant. Not good! It felt awful. Later, I thought about my tendency to fall into man-bashing and began to repair the bridge over the troubled waters of my mindset. I wanted to catch my thoughts while I was thinking and consciously change them to create a more honest and positive mental energy state. I wanted to quit the man-bashing habit and employ a more critical and balanced view of my relationships with men. The repairs began immediately. I still have a few to go. It's a process!

If we learn to build straight and strong bridges between how we think and act, our lives will be easier to navigate, even with the inevitable bumps and bruises. The sooner we do this, the better. It is an excellent use of energy to cultivate and deepen self-awareness. Even children get it.

This story comes from an experience I had while managing a yoga program at a summer camp for 750 kids ages five through twelve. In addition to classes and yoga clubs, we were trying out yoga interventions. If children were fighting or misbehaving and in danger of being suspended, they first saw one of the yoga teachers who taught them some basic calming and centering practices. One young boy who regularly got into fights learned a calming breath practice. After his session, he told the teacher, "I didn't know I had a choice about how I act."

He had begun to build a bridge between his body and mind, developing his ability to think critically about his actions.

The mind uses language, thoughts and emotions; the body and breath speak with feelings and sensations; and energy speaks through them all, sometimes adding in images and strong vibrations. If we know how to listen to and interpret those messages, things tend to go smoother in our daily lives.

When I finished writing this chapter, I sent M. a copy. She was as happy to get this answer as I was in giving it to her and now in sharing it with you.

Practice: Build Better Bridges
Quality to Embody: Connection

BUILDING BETTER BRIDGES ALLOWS THE ENERGY of witnessing to increase and strengthen the connections between body, breath/ energy and mind. These three exercises will help you tune into and interpret the messages you receive. You can do each one separately or string them together.

Align Your Energy

The Gesture of the Spine is an exercise that aligns energy. It is called "Merudanda mudra" in the yoga tradition, and helps to instill a sense of grounding and stability.

INSTRUCTIONS

1. Sit with your spine comfortably aligned.
2. Relax your chest and shoulders.
3. Make soft fists with your hands, thumbs extended.
4. Point the thumbs straight up.

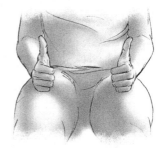

5. Rest the pinky sides of your hands on your knees or thighs.
6. Close your eyes or keep them slightly open with a downward gaze.
7. Breathe normally.
8. Hold for two to three minutes, or for as long as you are comfortable.

Relaxation Breath

The practice of Relaxation Breath brings awareness to how you are breathing, slows the number of breaths you take per minute, and lengthens your exhale. In turn, this calms the nervous system. It can be done anytime and anywhere to help you "chill out."

INSTRUCTIONS

1. Sit with your spine comfortably aligned.
2. Relax your chest and shoulders.
3. Close your eyes or keep them slightly open with a downward gaze.
4. Inhale normally.
5. Exhale normally.
6. Pause before taking a new breath and silently count: one thousand one, one thousand two.
7. Repeat.
8. Continue for two to three minutes, or longer if you are comfortable.

Left-Side, Right-Side Balancing Breath

The proper flow of oxygen and energy is necessary to maintain optimal health and a balanced outlook on life. Being aware of when you are most alert or drained and having readily available tools to respond to those feelings effectively will help you to live in better balance.

Here's one way to use your breath to balance your energy when you are feeling out of sorts.

INSTRUCTIONS

1. Sit and get comfortable.
2. Rest your hands in your lap.
3. Visualize inhaling through your left nostril.
4. Visualize exhaling through your right nostril.
5. Then visualize your next inhale coming in through your right nostril.
6. Visualize your exhale flowing out through your left nostril.
7. Repeat for two to three minutes, or as long as you like.
8. End by exhaling through the left nostril for calming or the right nostril for energizing.

Building bridges between our layers helps the messages we receive from them shine a light on the path we need to take to reach our goal of finding clarity, contentment and resilience.

SHOW UP AND BE HEARD

In the middle of this crazy world,
I'm just hoping I'll show up and be heard.

— Lyrics by Wah!

Everyone, including me, wants to show up and be heard. This may be why many of us find therapy helpful. When it works, therapy gives our voices the energy to show up and be heard. Even though we pay for the privilege, the experience can be healing. And yes, I am speaking from experience. I went into therapy to deal with an unhappy second marriage and ended up facing my issues of perfectionism and co-dependency.

When I say "heard," I don't mean heard as in, "you hear me talking until you can find a way to bring the conversation back to you." It means active listening, which is not the same as hearing sounds and noises.

Active, engaged listening requires holding space for a person to feel seen, understood, valued, respected and cared about. How we talk, when we talk, and what we talk about is the other side of the communication coin, and it is just as important as listening.

This is a major undertaking, and it's worth spending time to understand how our energy impacts and interacts with our communication style.

We all use and abuse our conversational energies. Our use of humor is one way to better understand our communication issues. As you read through this chapter, you will find a list of talker types, listening styles, and a few pop culture references that tickled my funny bone.

I've been struggling with being seen and heard for years. Energetically, it's exhausting. One time in the middle of a hissy fit, I told a co-worker I was seriously thinking about taking a vow of silence since no one was listening to me anyway. That may be because I am a Short Talker.

This speaking style is like newspaper headlines and breaking news banners on television. Short Talkers throw out words as bait to see if there is interest in what we have to say. If there is, we proceed. If not, we stop. We are horrified at the thought of boring people or holding communication hostages.

I'm an introverted Short Talker, sometimes a No Talker, but never a Close Talker. (You know, those people who get up in your face...) However, I am attracted to extroverts because they are Long Talkers. They tend to take up all the air in the room. There is no need for me to think or respond. And yes, I do understand that this sets me up to not be heard. It's complicated. I have issues.

On the flip side, am I a good listener? Many people have told me I am. Maybe that's because I'm an introvert. Unless I am asked a specific question and the person seems really interested, I tend to conserve my conversational energy and remain silent. That silence is often mistaken for listening. Sometimes I am listening, but at other times I'm not.

My active listening gene turns on when someone talks about subjects I'm interested in. I love talking about pop culture, humor, politics, food, health and wellness, adventure travel, world myster-ies, historical and cultural oddities, and the big questions: What is reality? Why are we here? Where did we come from? Where are we going? And what happens when we die?

Deep Talkers are as rare as a $2 bill. Those who share my inter-ests are my conversational soul mates. I enjoy, appreciate and think of them fondly long after our conversation is over, even if we have differing opinions.

My least favorite topics are what I call the K4P list—the unabridged activities of other people's Kids, Pets, Plants, Partners and Problems. Even so, it is important to listen to others talk about the things that interest them. I am trying to be a more empathetic listener. It's not easy or comfortable, but I'm working on it.

Regarding other people's problems, there is a caveat. I am happy to provide a listening ear for someone to talk or vent about a difficult situation. However, after three times listening to the same problem from the same person, my energy lags, my attention span shortens, and my listening gene shuts off. This is especially true if the situa-tion is unchanged and no attempts have been made to understand it, make progress toward a resolution, or accept that it is what it is. At that point, I am drowning in the drama and my silence is not active listening. I'd love to think of myself as being compassionate 24/7, 365 days a year, but I'm not. "And that's the truth."[15]

If I had to give a name to my listening style in these situations, I'd call myself a Surfer. I catch the top waves of the topic and ride it, tuning out the details, or troughs, if they drag on for longer than I can hang on. When that happens, I retreat into resentful, silent observation. It's an energy riptide that drags me down.

Ironically, I may be behaving in the same way as those I find myself judging. That means it's time to check myself, so I am. My

15 Catchphrase from the Edith Ann comedy sketches created by Lily Tomlin.

goal is to balance my energy in conversational exchanges while holding compassionate space to listen actively to others.

If this sounds familiar to you, try pre-planning solutions for a variety of communication scenarios you know you will face. Here are a few to consider.

Problem: Being interrupted

"Houston, we have a problem."[16] Being interrupted and asked a question for clarification or more information is okay. But when you're constantly interrupted and the conversation is pulled away before you've finished a thought, it can be irritating and frustrating. Serial interrupters suffer from a condition I call "Talkus Interruptus." Sometimes, they are aware of it, and sometimes not.

I have a friend who suffers from chronic Talkus Interruptus. One day, she admitted to a group of us at lunch that she was guilty of it and had traced it back to her childhood when interrupting was the only way she got to be heard in her family. Hearing that, I was less irritated by her interruptions because I understood the "why." However, there are others who don't seem to have a clue how often they interrupt. Here is one way to handle that situation without sinking into silent resentment.

Solution: Pre-plan a few stories

Recently, in anticipation of having dinner with friends, I wanted to tell a funny story about a recent viral trend called the "one chip challenge" in which participants eat a chip flavored with ghost pepper, the hottest pepper known to humankind. Then they post descriptions of their pain online. I rehearsed the story in my mind several times before dinner knowing I would be interrupted. Sure enough, one member of our group had heard about the challenge and interrupted me several times to tell it her way. This time, I was

---

16   From the movie *Apollo 13*, 1995.

ready. I ignored the interruptions and continued telling the story my way until she realized what she was doing and apologized.

Problem: Hostage situations

"Danger, Will Robinson!"[17] This is being caught and held in someone's energy net with a story that morphs from a Facebook post to a novel in just a few minutes. Until recently, I handled these situations by nodding or offering a half-hearted "Really?" "Oh my goodness," or "I can understand that" when they stopped to take a breath. My body lets me know I'm in a hostage situation by creating muscle spasms in my lower back. My mind follows up with feelings of being stuck, blocked and trapped.

After reflecting on the problem, I developed a list of Talker Type situations that needed solutions.

Long Talkers. When they start in, you can almost see them opening detailed files in their minds as they meticulously recount the contents of one and then proceed directly to the next. They have files on everything from their latest trip to what's going on with their relatives, kids, pets, work, hobbies and, of course, their health. They are what is known in Seinfeld-talk as the "unshushables."[18]

Side Trail Talkers. They take the longest route to the point they are making. They spin stories that are ultimately related to their main point, but by the time they get to it, everyone listening is exhausted. Well, maybe not everyone. But I am. It's hard to stay present in a situation like this. I wish they'd get to the point and

---

17 A reference to *Lost in Space*, an early science fiction TV show that aired from 1965-1968.

18 "There's always that certain group of people, isn't it? They're talking and talking, and everyone around them is shushing them and shushing them. They won't shush. They're the unshushables." From episode 10, "The Apartment," *Seinfeld* TV series, April 4, 1991.

"yada, yada, yada"[19] past the side trails. Yes, I lack patience, and I am aware of it.

Tornado Talkers. They have only one topic: complaints. They are the doom-and-gloomers. Their dark clouds blot out the sun of your good mood. Like a tornado, they start with moving gusts of air, which develops into an intense whirlwind that sucks you in and carries you along until it fizzles out or you find a way to escape. Tornado Talkers make me want to scream, "Serenity, now!"[20]

Solution. Realize you may have to interrupt to save your sanity

Go ahead and interrupt, but do it compassionately with full self-awareness.

The technique? Say with a smile, "I'm sorry to interrupt you." Then follow that line with a specific reason. You're late for a meeting, you have to meet a friend, or you have to "pay your water bill" before your bladder bursts. Never, ever say, "I don't mean to interrupt you," because you do.

That's how you disengage on your terms, without being rude, and it works 90 percent of the time.

ANOTHER ENERGY-DRAINING PROBLEM many introverts face is social gatherings.

Problem. The small talk scenario

It can be especially hard to be heard or to listen to others at events, like receptions, cocktail parties, fundraisers or dinner dances. These situations can be excruciatingly painful for introverts. Energetically,

---

19   In "The Yada Yada," episode 153 of the *Seinfeld* TV series, April 24, 1997, Marcy, George, Jerry and Elaine have a conversation in which they skip "boring" details and stick solely to the point.

20   "The Serenity Now," episode 159 of the Seinfeld TV series, October 9, 1997.

they last for years, instead of hours. The crowds, the noise, the effort to make small talk with friends, strangers or people you barely know can feel like torture. I don't feel seen or heard. And I know I'm not truly seeing or listening to others.

Solution. If you face this issue, try a small talk management list

Limit your exposure and attend only those events that are necessary. Pre-select a few small talk topics, like work, hobbies, weather and popular culture. Make eye contact and hold space for the situation, even when it's uncomfortable. As soon as you've small-talked with anyone on your friend or networking to-do list, employ the Irish goodbye[21] and leave quickly and quietly.

To manage both sides of the communication coin, take time to reflect long and deep on how you talk and how well you listen. It's easy to judge someone else's style, but it might actually be a reflection of your own.

Here's a poem I wrote to remind us how to show up and be heard and to see and hear others.

Show Up and Be Heard

To be seen and heard is both a tango and a duet.
To be successful, we must give as good as we get.
Shift happens when we witness what we think
and what we do.
Only then can we know what adjustments may
be due.
How we listen and how we talk requires
holding space.
We know we need to practice. We also need
some grace!

---

21 A slang phrase rumored to refer to a person ducking out of a party, social gathering or bad date without saying goodbye.

Practice: Still Waters Run Deep

Quality to Embody: Reflection

As you become aware of the communication situations that trigger you and leave you feeling stuck, tense, confused or drained, you will need techniques that can help bring your energy into balance. Here are three. They can be done anytime, anywhere.

Turtle in the Shell

This is an energy technique for feeling calm. Turtle in the Shell is called "Adhi mudra" in the yoga tradition. This hand gesture deepens a sense of grounding, moves energy out of the head, and promotes a feeling of safety and security.

INSTRUCTIONS

1. Stand or sit with your spine comfortably straight.
2. Place your thumbs (the turtle's head and neck) across your palms of your hands.
3. Make soft fists by folding your fingers (the turtle's shell) over your thumbs.
4. Rest your hands by the sides of your body if you are standing. If you are seated, place your hands on your knees or thighs. Be sure the back of your hands are facing up.
5. Hold for two to three minutes, or longer if you are comfortable.

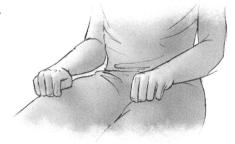

Focused Breathing

This can be done whenever you need calming and cooling to reduce inner tension.

Instructions

1. Stand or sit.
2. Allow your spine to be comfortably aligned.
3. Inhale normally.
4. Hold your breath and silently count to three.
5. Exhale normally.
6. Pause for a silent count to three.
7. Repeat for two to three minutes, or longer if you are comfortable.

Stand Your Ground

A shortened version of the Roots Visualization practice can be done whenever you need grounding and support to reduce inner tension. (For the full exercise, see page 162.)

Instructions

1. Turn your attention to the bottoms of your feet and feel your connection with the floor.
2. Visualize roots growing from the bottoms of your feet, branching and spreading deep into the earth.
3. Begin to draw in the grounding, stable, supportive energy of the earth.
4. Sense this energy filling your body from your toes to the crown of your head.
5. See and feel your entire body safe, stable and connected to the world as you stand your ground.

> *Energy doesn't communicate in English, French,*
> *Chinese or Swahili, but it does speak clearly.*

> — Elaine Seiler

NOBODY LOVES PERFECT

*We begin to find and become ourselves when
we notice how we are already found, already
truly, entirely, wildly, messily, marvelously
who we were born to be.*

— Anne Lamott

Many of us receive messages from school, home and society to strive for perfection in all our endeavors. While it may seem like a worthy goal, is it really? The pressure to be perfect can be a motivator or a source of anxiety.

Let's begin our exploration with some basic questions and answers.

What Is a Perfectionist?

PERFECTIONISM IS A MULTIDIMENSIONAL PERSONALITY CHAR-
ACTERISTIC. Perfectionists embody a mix of excessively high personal standards and overly critical self-evaluation and self-judgments.

There are three types of perfectionism.

- **Self-oriented perfectionism:** Having high expectations of self.
- **Socially prescribed perfectionism:** Embodying perfection to gain approval.
- **Other-oriented perfectionism:** Expecting others to hold the same standards.

Are Perfectionists Born That Way or Are They Made?

THAT'S THE OLD NATURE VERSUS NURTURE question. The results of a twin study showed there is a genetic component and also an environmental one. Children of highly critical parents or those who were raised in a chaotic disorganized home may be more prone to perfectionism. It turns out that perfectionism, like most everything else, is not either/or. It's both/and.[22]

Is Perfectionism Good or Bad?

IT DEPENDS. PERFECTIONISM HAS POSITIVE AND negative aspects.

The positive, or adaptive, perfectionist sets goals and enjoys the process of getting there. They can manage emotional attachments to the outcomes of their efforts and reframe the meaning of an experience that doesn't turn out as expected or hoped for. They have high standards, along with a healthy sense of self-worth.

The maladaptive perfectionist has an unhealthy urge or inner push to be perfect in every aspect of their life. Their eye is always

---

22   Iranzo-Tatay C, Gimeno-Clemente N, Barberá-Fons M, Rodriguez-Campayo MÁ, Rojo-Bofill L, Livianos-Aldana L, Beato-Fernandez L, Vaz-Leal F, Rojo-Moreno L. "Genetic and environmental contributions to perfectionism and its common factors." *Psychiatry Res.* 2015 Dec. europepmc.org/article/med/26611155.

on the goal. When that goal is reached, the next one automatically replaces it. These perfectionists do not enjoy the process of getting to the goal. They have an unhealthy level of self-criticism and self-judgment when things don't turn out well and feel inadequate even when things turn out as planned. Nothing, especially themselves, is ever good enough. As you might imagine, this can have a major impact on one's mental health and well-being.[23]

I used to be a maladaptive perfectionist, but I am in recovery. What helped me most was the wish to recover, the strength to take on the task, and a sense of humor to help me through. This quote from Reba McEntire sums it up.

To succeed in life, you need three things: a wishbone,
a backbone and a funny bone.

- **My wishbone:** I wish I could always see myself with clarity and be content with what I find.

- **My backbone:** It took backbone to start this self-awareness journey of recovery and stay on it, but turning back is not an option.

- **My funny bone:** Humor saved me. It is good medicine.

So, how do I know I'm a perfectionist? My therapist told me.

I was in an unhappy second marriage. Counseling failed when my husband refused to continue. So, I spilled my sad story in run-on sentences and heavy paragraphs to my no-nonsense, down-to-earth social psychologist. She listened, then told me in no uncertain terms I was a perfectionist with co-dependency issues, and I'd have to deal with that before we could even talk about the marriage. My mouth dropped open. I was mad. I didn't believe her, so I checked out a few

---

23   Peter J Bieling, Anne L Israeli, Martin M Antony, "Is perfectionism good, bad, or both? Examining models of the perfectionism construct." *Personality and Individual Differences*, Volume 36, Issue 6, 2004. doi.org/10.1016/S0191-8869(03)00235-6.

books from the library and discovered she was right. I had to admit it. I am a perfectionist, and I was closer to the edge of maladaptive perfectionism than I was comfortable with.

My brand of perfectionism was exhausting, and it took many units of mental and physical energy to keep up that "perfect" persona. What it was doing to my life and well-being was not funny, but I knew if I didn't find a way to laugh my way out, I'd drown in an ocean of tears, which would not be a good look for someone striving to be perfect in all things.

There are some disturbing side effects of maladaptive perfectionism. The list is long and scary, but here are a few highlights.

- **Control issues.** Yeah, that's real.
- **Obsessive-compulsive disorder.** Uh-oh! My closets are tightly organized by season, aligned by color and arranged by tops, pants, jackets, dress clothes and shoes. More of the same with my linen closets and kitchen cabinets.
- **Workaholism.** Hmm... That sounds familiar.
- **Low self-esteem.** *Sigh.* Yeah, pretty sure that's a factor.
- **Anxiety, panic attacks and depression.** I got depressed reading about this!
- **Substance abuse.** I sure hope chocolate doesn't count.
- **Chronic stress.** Maybe that was the source of the bald spots, skin rashes and constipation I dealt with during my menopause transition.
- **Heart disease.** Bummer! That one runs in the family.
- **Thoughts of suicide.** Research says perfectionists are more likely to kill themselves than regular, mediocre-performing people. Yikes! Fortunately, I'm in recovery, and I like myself too much to deprive the world of whatever talents I have left to share.

With all those symptoms, I had to wonder why there was no cure. They have pills, patches and prescriptions for everything else, so why not perfectionism? If the American Medical Association ever declares perfectionism a disease, we'll have a pill for it in no time. The drug industry would be on that like white on rice. And if we had a drug, it could be called "Perfectomayacin." One pill a day and perfectionism goes away.

But then we'd have to consider the side effects since all drugs have them. They come right along with the fix. TV commercials filled with smiling men and women running through grassy fields, walking hand in hand, or playing with puppies would first extol the benefits of Perfectomayacin and then follow up with the side effects, which might include the following:

- Do not take Perfectomayacin if you are nursing, pregnant or may become pregnant. I'm postmenopause, so no need to worry about that one.

- Taking Perfectomayacin may cause impotence. Another side effect I can definitely rule out.

- Do not eat sweets or drink alcohol if you are taking Perfectomayacin. What? Dessert is my favorite food group. And I do like a vodka tonic now and then.

- Perfectomayacin may cause mood swings or behavior changes, like depression, anxiety or panic attacks. Wait a minute. Didn't we just see that depression, anxiety and panic attacks are symptoms of perfectionism?

- Use of Perfectomayacin may result in drowsiness, dizziness, nasal irritation, insomnia, nausea and projectile vomiting. That would definitely destroy my image at a meeting or social gathering, but then maybe I wouldn't care since, thanks to Perfectomayacin, I'd no longer be a perfectionist!

- Taking Perfectomayacin may cause headaches, trouble concentrating, and memory problems. I know I don't want to remember any of this.

Maybe my recovery process would have been faster if Perfectomayacin had been available, but the slower process of working through my five layers of self-awareness to unearth the reasons I'd chosen perfectionism as a coping mechanism in the first place seemed a better use of my energy.

With no external quick fix available from the outside, I took a look inside and found my perfectionist behavior reflected five key obstacles to self-awareness. They are:

1. Ignorance

   - **Then:** I used to think I was always right and superior to others.

   - **Now:** My ignorance has been reduced by half, and I see more clearly I'm not superior to anyone else. (Only to a few members of my family and a couple of friends and colleagues. Remember, I'm in recovery. It's a process.)

2. Ego

   - **Then:** If someone did something lame, dumb or disorganized (in my opinion) in my presence, the situation would lead to a three-layer meltdown resulting in the urge to say, "I know what your problem is. I have time to tell you about it, and I have a complete list of all the things you need to do to fix yourself."

   - **Now:** With practice, the meltdowns are fewer. I've learned to zip my lip, and I don't give advice unless I'm asked for it. (Most of the time, anyway. I'm in recovery. It's a process.)

3. Unhealthy attachment to outcomes

   • **Then:** I'd dot every "i" and cross every "t" because it *had* to be perfect. But it was never perfect (to my standards), and the emotional spiral of deflation, anger and guilt kicked in, followed by my grand defense mechanism, the blame game. It's someone else's fault.

   • **Now:** I understand there are only four results to anything I do: what I expect, more than I expect, less than I expect, or the unexpected and—spoiler alert—I can't control any of them and none of them will ever be perfect. This one is *hard*. It sucks wind! But I'm in recovery. It's a process.

4. Unreasonable dislikes

   • **Then:** I disliked other perfectionists because they acted like they were better than me.

   • **Now:** OMG, maybe they were! I understand they're okay, I'm okay, you're okay, everyone is okay. (Well, except for a few members of my family and a couple of friends and colleagues. Remember, I'm in recovery. It's a process.)

5. Fear of being found out as a fake and a fraud

   • **Then:** It's the imposter syndrome; a belief that if people really knew me, they'd see I'm a fake. Then they wouldn't like me and that could intensify symptoms, like anxiety, low self-esteem and workaholism. (Sigh.) What to do?

   Let it go. I have to give props for my recovery formula to former Senator Al Franken and the movie he made while working as a comedian called *Stuart Saves His Family*.

Regarding fear, Stuart says, "Face it, trace it, and erase it." Because I don't want to forget what I've come through, I don't want to erase anything. To keep this advice in line with the five layers of self-awareness, I re-framed it as, "Face it, trace it, embrace it, and then replace it."

- **Now:** Once I was able to get some clarity around my issues and started to address them, I discovered the energetic intensity of my perfectionism decreased. And yes, there were some side effects, but they were all good. I learned to enlighten up. I lead a more balanced, contented and resilient life. (About 80 percent of the time... Remember, I'm in recovery. It's a process.)

As part of my recovery, I wrote a poem about the fruitlessness of perfectionism gone wrong. Here it is.

Perfect

Seeking love, she took her cue
From the folks on Madison Avenue
Sad way to go
She doesn't know
That nobody loves perfect.

Her clothes a top designer line
Laurent, Givenchy, Blass and Kline
They fit just so
She doesn't know
That nobody loves perfect

She holds so much of life inside
And watches, waits and hopes to find
The peace, the joy, the happiness
Of love—the perfect kind
Every lacquered hair in place

A plastic smile upon her face
Makeup just so
She doesn't know
That nobody loves perfect

Practice: Building Consistency
Quality to Embody: Discipline

OF THE NINE MEANINGS OF THE word "discipline," one embodies the energy of a consistent practice, which is needed for this journey. If you find your brand of perfectionism, or some other difficulty, is impacting your life in an unhelpful way and sapping your energy, the following exercises may be helpful.

Expanding Openness

The Gesture of Expansiveness is an exercise that produces openness, clarity and the ability to see things in a new way. It is called "Urdhavm-Merudanda mudra" in the yoga tradition. This hand gesture cultivates an upward flowing energetic sense of optimism and vitality.

INSTRUCTIONS

This can be done with your eyes opened or closed.

1. Stand or sit with your spine comfortably straight.
2. Curl your fingers into the palms of your hands.
3. Extend your thumbs.
4. Rest the backs of your hands on your thighs or knees.
5. Point your thumbs out to the sides.
6. Relax your shoulders.
7. Hold for two to three minutes, or longer if you are comfortable.

Crocodile Pose

This posture works with the first three layers: body, breath and mind. It encourages a relaxed state of awareness and helps you breathe slowly, efficiently and deeply. It can also ease anxiety and stress, as well as promote sleep.

INSTRUCTIONS

1. Lie down on your stomach with your legs comfortably apart.
2. Fold your arms in front of your body, resting your hands on your upper arms.
3. Rest your forehead on your arms.
4. Allow your legs to flop open with your toes pointing out (or in), whichever is most comfortable.
5. Begin to watch the natural flow of your breath. Focus your awareness on your belly. In this position, feel your breath moving into your ribs and abdomen.

6. Close your eyes and let your whole body melt into the surface you are lying on.
7. Notice how your belly presses into the floor when you inhale (or into the mattress if you are doing this in bed).
8. With each exhale, allow your body to relax a bit more.
9. Practice for five to ten minutes, or longer if you are comfortable.
10. To come out, bring your palms under your shoulders and slowly press up onto your hands and knees.

11. Sit back onto your heels. Pause here and, when you are ready, bring yourself up to seated or standing. If practicing in bed, roll over and go to sleep!

The Mind Drift

Allowing the mind to drift holds space for what you want to work on. In this exercise, you choose the condition, issue or situation you want to work with and let the mind drift to see what thoughts, memories or feelings surface. Of course, the mind will wander and there will be distractions, but this practice asks that you watch them when they arise and hold space for them as well.

The focus of the practice is on the process, not the outcome, even though the outcome may call for some type of action or response. You may need more than one session to trace and get comfortable enough to embrace what you find. Go slowly.

There are no hard-and-fast rules on how to do this practice as everyone has their preferences. Sometimes, insights pop to mind fully formed. Other times, you catch a slim thread of thought and follow it to an insight, while still other times nothing comes but more confusion. This is an organic and fluid practice. It takes time, but it can be a deeply satisfying and productive use of your energy.

Instructions

Face It: Write down or state your condition, issue or situation. Bring yourself to a comfortable position, seated or lying down. Play soft soothing music if that helps your process. Let your mind drift.

Trace It: Take time to explore any sensations or symptoms that might be manifesting in your body, your breath, or your thoughts and emotions.

Remember, if there is an imbalance in one layer, it may show up in one or all of the others. Watch for any nuggets of awareness, memories, connection or wisdom that float up from the subconscious mind. As you drift, know that many thoughts and emotions, even contradictory ones, can be present simultaneously.

Can you welcome and witness all that is present without judgment or do you notice resistance? Ease and soften attachment to any negative thoughts, difficult emotions or behaviors that cause you discomfort, concern or difficulty.

If you experience discomfort or resistance, imagine or visualize a thick glass wall between you and what is making you uncomfortable. This creates distance between you and what is floating up. Over time, the emotional charge will gradually lessen in intensity once you have shined the light of self-awareness onto it.

Embrace it: Can you welcome what you find? If not, be compassionate with yourself. Accept that these thoughts, emotions and behaviors exist as your guides and teachers.

Replace it: Replace unhelpful attitudes, beliefs and behaviors with helpful ones. Here are a few examples.

Unhelpful	Helpful
I am not good enough.	I'm good enough, warts and all.
I'll never get this right.	I always do my level best.
I can't trust anybody.	I trust myself.
Everybody judges me.	I accept constructive criticism.

When you feel your mind drift is complete, write, journal or draw anything that stood out to you. Decide if you wish to take an action, make a change, or let things be as they are with full knowledge of the consequences.

Your Third Layer of Self-Awareness: Mental

The Taittiriya Upanishad suggests the best way to work with this layer is to cultivate a desire to learn, willingness and diligence to do the work, the courage to persevere, and the honesty to accept and work with the outcomes of what you find—all of it—the good, the bad, the beautiful and the ugly.

When we think of the mind, we often include the brain and the idea of consciousness. These words are frequently used interchangeably, but in reality, there are differences we need to understand in order to get a clear picture of our third layer of self-awareness.

The Brain

HIPPOCRATES WAS THE FIRST PERSON (that we know of) to claim that the brain is the seat of consciousness. The brain is a visible, tangible part of the physical body. It weighs about 3.3 lb. (1.5 kg) and makes up about 2 percent of a human's body weight. The brain contains billions of nerve fibers, which are connected by trillions of synapses.

Scientists study the brain to understand how brain activity is connected to how we think and behave. They used to believe the human brain is fixed at birth with a set of cognitive abilities, which remain hardwired for our lifespan. Research has recently found the human brain can change, grow and evolve. The word for this is "neuroplasticity." It means the neurons in our brains are pliable. The latest research now views the intricate working of our brain as continually reconfiguring itself in response to experience, learning and injury.

New studies have found nerve cells from the brain in other parts of the body; another indication of just how connected everything is. Our gut has more than 100 million neurons and the heart, 40,000 neurons. The head, heart and gut communicate with each other neurologically, biochemically, biophysically and energetically. Unlike the mind, during an autopsy, our brain can be seen, touched and dissected.

The Mind

THE MIND IS THAT INTANGIBLE PART of ourselves consisting of thoughts, emotions, ego, personality, attitudes, beliefs, imagination, perception and judgment. This is how we think, what we think about, how we express our emotions, what we pay attention to, and how we relate to ourselves, others and life in general. The mind is not physical. During an autopsy, it cannot be seen, touched or dissected.

The tasks of the mind are to think, plan, analyze, judge, critique and warn. Our thoughts and emotions are tools to help us perceive and understand what is happening within and around us. The mind does this in two ways.

The first is by analyzing and organizing knowledge and experiences (left brain). This happens when we understand how our thoughts, ego, personality, attitudes, beliefs and imagination work to nourish and challenge us every minute of every day. Self-awareness practices, like journaling, self-reflection and meditation, help us work with our thoughts and emotions so we can be more mentally, psychologically and spiritually healthy.

The second is by honing our intuition, creativity and openness to receiving instant knowing (right brain). When right brain intuition and gut feelings kick in, we experience *aha* moments that lead to awareness and clarity about how we navigate the joys and sorrows of living in our five-sense material world.

Understanding the mind with its thoughts, emotions and belief systems is key to cultivating self-awareness. Suppressing, repressing or trying to rid ourselves of difficult thoughts, emotions or experiences is not helpful. The real goal is to recognize, become aware of, acknowledge and accept what we find with compassion and without judgment. The next step is deciding to take whatever action is necessary to help us move toward clarity, contentment and internal resilience.

Think of the mind as an iceberg. The top one-third is our everyday conscious mind. The middle third is the subconscious, or preconscious, mind that is not easily accessed or seen, and the deepest bottom third is our unconscious mind.

The following descriptions provide a summary of these psychological dimensions of the mind and how each can be connected to and interrelate with the five layers of self-awareness.

The Conscious Mind

This is the mental state that we associate with who we are. Our conscious mind communicates to our inner selves and the outside world through speech, pictures, writing, physical movement and thoughts. It consists of everything inside our wakeful awareness.

This dimension of mind is what we use when we pay attention to our physical body and our surroundings. At this level, the mind is primarily concerned with our need to avoid pain, repeat pleasure, and connect with others.

The conscious mind relates primarily to the first two layers of self-awareness: physical and energetic.

The Subconscious Mind

The subconscious is also known as the preconscious mind. It consists of accessible information that we become aware of when we direct our attention to it. This dimension of the mind is like a holding tank for a vast collection of beliefs, ideas and reactions to life around us that drives our lives without our having to think about every move or step. For example, we can drive home from work or from a visit with friends without having to consciously navigate by thinking, *Now I turn right, then a left, and then straight ahead for 3.5 miles.* Our feet are doing their job on the gas and the brake pedals, our hands work the steering wheel, and unless we encounter a snag in traffic, roadwork or an accident, we are usually relaxed.

This dimension of the mind is also responsible for our involuntary actions, like breathing and heart rate. This dimension of the mind communicates with us through feelings, emotions, imagination, sensations, intuitive wisdom, our "sixth sense," *aha* moments and dreaming awareness.

The subconscious mind can influence our judgments, feelings or behavior. When we set an intention to cultivate self-awareness and tap into the deeper dimensions of the mind, we can uncover our beliefs and memories, as well as the reasons for our habits and interactions with the outside world.

This dimension of the mind is thought to relate to the next two layers of self-awareness: mental and intuitive wisdom.

The Unconscious Mind

Our feelings, motives and decisions are powerfully influenced by our past experiences and are stored in the bottom third of our mental iceberg: the unconscious. These experiences can be joyful, scary, unhelpful, disturbing, blissful or spiritual, to name just a few.

We accept that some unconscious material will need a strong, specific trigger to bring them to the conscious mind. Some tools used for this purpose are meditation, dreaming and hypnosis.

This dimension is thought to relate to the fifth layer of self-awareness: bliss (a connection to something larger than ourselves).

Consciousness

WHAT DOES IT MEAN TO BE conscious? That depends on who you ask and what level of being conscious you want to work on. Consciousness at its simplest is awareness of our existence and everything we experience: joys, sorrows and everything in between. It is the most familiar, and yet the most mysterious, aspect of our lives.

The nature of consciousness is one of the great unanswerable questions. We all know we are conscious beings, but what is consciousness? How are we aware of our own nature? How does our consciousness differ from other people or animals?

Both the mind and the brain are involved in the question of consciousness. So we might ask, "Is consciousness in the mind or is the mind in consciousness?" Science, philosophy and metaphysics have differing theories, concepts and beliefs about the answers to that question.

Scientific research on the relationship between the brain, mind and human consciousness has proved challenging because of the vast differences and difficulty in measuring individual subjective experiences.

For millennia, philosophy and metaphysics have told us the brain is merely the physical component that links the mind to consciousness, but that consciousness itself is the first, foremost and truest reality. The concepts, models and practices they provide are meant to help us realize the ultimate reality of that consciousness often referred to as "enlightenment."

The study of mind and consciousness is at the heart of the self-awareness journey. Because we need to start where we are, this book suggests ways to begin the work by first grounding us in the here and now before moving into the mystery (or not).

Here is one way to think about the question of brain, mind and consciousness. When consciousness is predominately focused in the mind, our awareness is generally on the five-sense material world and *what* we think, feel and do (the third layer of self-awareness).

Here's an example.

- **Thinking:** Why is traffic so backed up? I'm going to be late for class.
- **Feeling:** I am frustrated and irritated.
- **Behavior:** My lips are tight and my hands are drumming the steering wheel.

When the mind is aware of an expanded consciousness, we can uncover material from the deeper layers of our mental iceberg to learn *why* we think, feel and act as we do (the fourth layer of self-awareness). Then our choices for expressing ourselves become conscious and self-aware.

Here's an example of that.

- **Thinking:** Traffic is backed up. I'm going to be late for class. I'll have to wait. It is what it is.

- **Feeling:** I feel frustrated and irritated. I don't like waiting. It brings up a fear of not being in control.
- **Behavior:** I'll take some deep breaths, put on some relaxing music and wait. If traffic doesn't clear up in ten minutes, I'll call to let them know I'll be late. It is what it is.

The relationship between the brain, mind and consciousness is a question that may wait a long time for a definitive answer. The key takeaway is to recognize how interrelated and interconnected they are with each other and with who we are and hope to become.

To understand our life's lessons, we need to tune into the dimensions of the mind to perceive and consciously change, reframe or accept what we find. We can do this by turning our attention to the third and fourth steps of the Nine Steps to Self-Awareness.

Step 3. Identify Your Thoughts and Feelings

- What am I thinking?
- Are my thoughts focused on the past? The future? My current situation?
- Am I trying to solve a problem?
- What am I feeling? Can I label the emotion? Is it pleasant or upsetting?
- Am I feeling more than one emotion at the same time?
- Is there a pattern to my thoughts and emotions?

Step 4. Explore Your Beliefs

- What do I believe about my current situation?
- Is it connected to what I believe about myself?
- Is it something I believe about others?

- Is it something I believe about my life?
- Is there a pattern to my beliefs?
- Does this pattern lead to helpful or unhelpful thoughts, emotions and behaviors?

Most of us do not have a full understanding of how we think and feel or what we believe. Engaging and grappling with the mind at this level is not how we want to spend the little free time we have when we're not working, volunteering, parenting, caretaking, paying bills or managing our daily to-do lists. However, if we want to move closer to the goal of self-awareness, we need to choose to do that—one small step at a time.

Here is a contemporary version of a Cherokee story that illustrates this point.

> One evening an old Cherokee woman told her granddaughter about a battle that goes on inside people. She said, "My daughter, the battle is between two wolves inside us all. One is our shadow. It is ignorance, ego, attachment, aversion and fear. The other is our self-awareness: clarity, contentment and resilience."
>
> The little girl thought about it for a minute and then said "*Elisi* (Grandmother), which one wins?"
>
> The old Cherokee woman replied, "*Ulisi* (Granddaughter), the one you feed."

The chapters in this section will share personal stories and experiences about working with positive and unhelpful thoughts, emotions, beliefs and attitudes toward self. The practices focus on acceptance, understanding, diligence and assertiveness techniques to help you feed your self-awareness wolf.

DON'T BELIEVE
EVERYTHING YOU THINK

You can believe something really hard...
and still be wrong.

— Jodi Picoult

Oh, the crazy things we believed as children!

My friend Laurie fell off a swing while hanging upside down. She fractured her sternum, spent weeks with a taped chest, and for years believed she would never develop breasts.

I believed that to get married, I would have to go door-to-door to find a husband. As a young girl, I used to sit on the sofa in the living room, stare out the window, and think about knocking on my neighbors' doors to ask if there was anyone in the house who would be interested in marrying me. As an introvert, that prospect was terrifying. I have no idea where that belief came from, but I know that I believed it.

When I asked my son if he could remember ever believing anything strange or weird, he declined to answer for himself (I wonder why?) but offered that one of his childhood friends would not eat bread crusts because someone told her they were made of baked worms.

A belief is a thought we hold to be true even though we may not be able to prove it. When proof arrives through the process of education, experience and critical thinking, our perception can change to acknowledge the belief as false and unhelpful or to realize its truth. Fortunately for Laurie, my son's friend and me, time, knowledge and experience proved our childhood beliefs to be false. Even so, attachment to certain beliefs that defy truth and evidence can impact our lives for years.

Laurie developed breasts, but the emotional effect of the accident left her extremely anxious about hanging upside down. She told me this during an aerial yoga class while I was helping her into a back straddle (hanging upside down with legs wrapped around the aerial hammock). She was not able or ready to overcome her fear.

I learned that the path to marriage was to date potential mates until you found "The One" who would be your partner until death or divorce do you part.

I don't know for certain if my son's friend ever got over the baked-worm bread crust belief, but I'm pretty sure they did.

Some beliefs are helpful and productive. We believe a balanced diet, regular exercise, and supportive social connections will keep us healthy as we age. The proof? There is good research focused on the benefits of healthy living.

But even if we choose to follow these guidelines, we have no guarantee how they'll play out in the long run. Stuff happens! Despite there being no guarantees, I know my belief in balanced living will keep me exercising without taking too many days off, eating nutritious food my body digests well (with a few cheat days here and there), and practicing yoga and meditation both on and off the mat.

Other beliefs are unhelpful and unproductive. For example, I once believed asking for help was a sign of weakness. In my life, this belief often co-existed with feeling angry, stressed and overwhelmed with responsibility. It was negatively affecting my peace of mind. When I reached my breaking point, I knew I needed a change, so I asked myself a question. "Where did that belief come from?" With reflection, I was able to trace it to its source—to watching my mom, my Aunt Lucy, and my favorite cousin Ella seemingly do it all. I watched them take on responsibility for family life, work outside the home, community involvement, and church projects.

The key word here, as you may have guessed, is "seemingly." I am sure they could have used help, but I never heard or saw them ask for it. Why? I can guess. It might be that strong Black woman stereotype or the independent streak many of us carry. Remember the line from the Helen Reddy song, "I am woman, hear me roar?"

Anyway, I'll never know for sure. My mom, aunt and cousin have all passed, so I can't ask them. I was left dealing with a lingering and possibly neurotic emotional attachment to that belief. I'm very uncomfortable being dependent on and obligated to others.

Recently, I discovered this discomfort might run in the family and across gender lines. At a family gathering, I was talking to my son about this, telling him how I felt, and when I got to the part about understanding why I was reluctant to ask for or accept help when offered, he nodded in agreement and said, "I'm too independent, and I don't like feeling obligated." OMG! The light bulb went off. Finally, I understood his reaction whenever I offered to help him. It was always, "Thanks, but I can handle it." I was able to help out with furniture for his new apartment only when I offered it as a birthday present.

Hearing that from my son helped me understand myself. It was my emotional attachment to the belief about asking for help and feeling obligated that caused my stress and discomfort. Once I recognized that, I learned to think clearly about asking for help and accepting it with gratitude when offered. I no longer believe it's a sign of weakness. (Well, most of the time. It's a process.)

My strategy for changing this unhelpful belief is to use a positive resolve, often referred to as an "affirmation." I prefer the word, "resolve" because it means to find a solution to a problem. It can work wonders if used regularly. With practice, we learn how to take another view, reframe an unhelpful perspective, and minimize unproductive emotional attachments. Think of a resolve as the new and improved version of a New Year's resolution.

We make New Year's resolutions to set big goals and dedicate time and energy trying to reach them. The most common resolutions are typically about self-care, losing weight, kicking the smoking habit or other addictions, and making more money. Sadly, according to statistics, our efforts to effect those changes are dropped long before the year is up.

I confess I have made resolutions like those in the past—made 'em and broke 'em. Here are a few.

- I will lose fifteen pounds this year.
- I will stick to a budget.
- I am going to learn to speak Brazilian Portuguese.

Like I said, made 'em and broke 'em.

But a positive resolve is different. For starters, it is set in the present tense. It is meant to work on a significant self-awareness goal, and its focus is long-term.

In my case, I needed two resolves.

My Unhelpful Belief	My Positive Resolve
Asking for help is a sign of weakness.	I ask for help when I need it.
I can do it all myself.	I gratefully accept help when it is offered.

Notice the present tense wording, "I ask" and "I accept," instead of "I will" or "I am going to." Making a resolve asks us to assume that what we hope to achieve is already true.

To put my resolves into action, I wrote them down and taped them to the refrigerator and my bathroom mirror so they were visible every day. I repeated them often, silently or aloud, as I moved through my day. That way, they stayed present and mentally handy when I found myself needing help but resisting asking for it or accepting it when offered.

Happily, with time and practice, my emotional attachment to the belief that asking for help is a sign of weakness is gradually losing its charge and its power. I still think about it. I still feel it, but I no longer believe it because it is being transformed from an unhealthy reaction into a positive response. The words "please" and "thank you" are now spoken more genuinely and comfortably. I am more comfortable depending on others for help and, in terms of obligation, am happy to return a favor if and when the opportunity presents itself and, if it doesn't, I make an effort to pay it forward and spread the positive energy.

Practice: Create a Positive Resolve
Quality to Embody: Diligence

WORKING WITH UNHELPFUL THOUGHTS AND BELIEFS requires diligence. To act with diligence means to be thorough. Diligence requires patience and practice along with the ability to persevere and persist. Begin by becoming clear about which thought or belief is adversely affecting your peace of mind. This process asks you to be honest with yourself. The work takes time, but the juice will be worth the squeeze.

Use positive resolves to take a deeper dive into your self-awareness. It's best to work with the same resolve until your goal is reached, whether that's over a few months, a few years, or a lifetime. Creating and working with a resolve is meant to remind you of what is already true so you don't have to apply ego, willpower or striving. In the yoga tradition, positive resolves are said to bring longer-lasting results, so when you write yours, remember to avoid the negative. Instead of "I won't eat sugar," think "I eat healthy and well-balanced meals." Instead of "I won't smoke," think "I live a smoke-free life."

Creating a positive resolve requires time and careful thinking. Here's how to do it.

INSTRUCTIONS

1. **Find your resolve.** A few lines from a character in one of my short stories will illustrate this concept. Over lunch, Miss Millie, a spiritual healer, is sharing wisdom with a woman seeking help for a midlife identity crisis. Miss Millie tells her to, "Ask the important questions. Become quiet. Listen within for the answers. Be diligent. Be patient. Trust your process and be brave."

   Consider an unhelpful thought or belief you'd like to change, then write down the opposite thought—your resolve. Start with a short positive statement made in the present tense. This will shift and reframe your awareness and attention from the unhelpful to the positive. Here are some examples.

My Unhelpful Belief	My Positive Resolve
I can't trust anybody.	I trust myself.
I'll never be happy.	I enjoy life. I'm content.
I don't fit in anywhere.	I am unique.
I don't deserve anything.	I have everything I need.
I'm too _____ (fat, short, tall, etc.).	I accept myself as I am.

| I'll always feel_____ | I manage my feelings |
| (sad, afraid, angry, etc.). | and seek help if I can't. |

Notice that the first two words of the positive resolve are stated in the present tense.

If you choose to use this technique for more practical matters, like losing weight or expanding your business, you can word your resolve this way:

* I am a healthy weight.
* I am a successful business owner.

2. **Remember your resolve.** You can remind yourself of your intention by writing it on sticky notes and tacking them to your refrigerator, closet door or bathroom mirror. They will act as daily reminders. You can journal about it, noting any blocks, obstacles, thoughts or emotions that arise around it. You can state it silently or aloud.

In this way, your reminders may "pop" when you wake up in the morning, drive to work, exercise, cook, clean or at any other time during the day. Keeping your resolve alive enables you to make conscious mid-course corrections to return to your path if you take a detour and get lost, and you will. Remember, you are a work in progress.

DECONSTRUCTING YOUR EMOTIONAL PALETTE

We cannot heal what we cannot feel.

— John Bradshaw

The words "emotion" and "feeling" are often used interchangeably, but science perceives emotions and feelings as two closely related, but distinct, things. Emotions are physical responses to stimuli that begin deep in the brain and result in physical sensations and biochemical reactions that can be measured. Feelings, on the other hand, are said to be the result of having emotions. They are mental associations and reactions to emotions. What we feel is influenced by our experiences, beliefs and memories. Unlike emotions, feelings can be difficult to measure accurately. Fascinating. Who knew?

However, to identify how many emotions we have, we'll need to tiptoe through a minefield of differing opinions. And spoiler alert! There is no consensus.

Some experts say there are eight emotions: joy, trust, fear, surprise, sadness, disgust, anger and anticipation. Some identify six:

happiness, sadness, surprise, fear, anger and disgust. Others, five: anger, fear, grief, joy and love. And some say four: anger, fear, happiness and sadness, while still others say as many as ninety!

When I began to explore this for myself, I decided to rely on my own experience, understanding and personal emotional palette. Why a palette? It seemed like a perfect metaphor for deconstructing my emotions.

A palette is a board an artist uses to choose, sort and mix colors. There is a real palette on my living room wall. The artist, Stanwyk Cromwell, submitted an artfully re-imagined palette for his 50-year retrospective exhibit at the art center in my town. I saw it and had to have it. It's full of color and artful designs. At the top are the artist's tools, a palette knife and a brush.

In this metaphor, the palette board is the mind-space: clean, clear and empty until the knife positions, spreads and mixes emotions in solid blocks and swirling layers all over it. Then the brush dips into the blocks and layers to color our emotional lives daily. Some of those emotional paintings are full of sadness, regret, anger and fear, while others are bright, sun-filled, creative, happy and content.

Our job is to deconstruct and understand these paintings. When we're ready to meet that challenge with a bit of wisdom and balance, we can find clarity, contentment and resilience.

To work with my emotional palette, I decided to go with the ones that made the most sense to me:

- anger
- fear
- happiness
- sadness

I can easily feel the physical sensations these four have in my body. The many shades and gradations of my feelings can be sourced from those four. And since this is my experience, I'm the only one who has to be okay with it. So I'm good to go.

In the palette for my emotions, I have included their colors, some shadings and feelings I experience and a few I don't. I've included where these sensations appear in my body as of this writing, in this stage of my life. I expect that may change over time.

Anger

An emotion of displeasure, irritation, frustration or hostility, often as a result of mistreatment or opposition.

Color

Red, as in "seeing red."

Shades

There are many shades of anger. I found over sixty ranging from mild irritation to full-blown rage. Understanding them helps me identify where I am on the continuum. Here are a few.

- **Annoyance:** Experiencing something as irritating, bothersome or displeasing.
- **Frustration:** A sensation of being blocked or prevented from achieving the desired outcome.
- **Indignant:** Righteous anger or disgust at what appears to be unjust, unfair or mean.
- **Furious:** A strong sense of displeasure or hostility, often the result of mistreatment or opposition.
- **Enraged:** Uncontrolled anger expressed in violent action or speech.

Understanding the shades of anger is helpful. Knowing I'm annoyed, frustrated, indignant or furious helps me respond with a bit more clarity and balance to whatever situation has triggered one or more of those shades.

I have an intimate relationship with several shades of anger. Fortunately, rage is not one of them.

What makes me angry? It's being kept waiting, being ignored, disrespected, constantly interrupted, or lied to. So, basically, I can fluctuate from mild irritation to being pissed off or furious several times on any given day.

Location and Felt Sense

That depends. If it's annoyance and frustration, I feel it in my neck and head with prickly sensations around my eyes, jaw and mouth. When feeling stuck or blocked, I feel it in my lower back and right hip. It changes if I'm furious or indignant. If you read the chapter "Building Bridges," you learned about my "volcano incident," when my husband was late to pick up my stepson and I had another commitment. When that happened, the anger started in my belly, then went systemwide like a volcano spewing boiling lava.

When I feel righteous anger about racism, sexism, war and social injustice, it's the same. But rather than exploding, my volcano rumbles and spits. I know it's active and trying to figure out how, when and where to express itself, while I decide if there is anything I'm willing to do to face those issues. Instead of mumbling, cursing or flipping my middle finger, literally or mentally, I can choose a more productive response.

Fear

An uncomfortable emotion or inner alarm that results from something we recognize, resist or perceive as a danger or a threat.

Color

Some people say black, but mine is more of a dark, muddy brown.

Shades

- **Insecurity:** A sense of being disoriented, unconfident or uneasy.

- **Anxiety:** Apprehension that something bad, unpleasant or stressful will happen.

- **Alarm:** Discomfort about something recognized or perceived as a danger or threat.

- **Panic:** A strong sense of fright, horror, terror or trepidation.

- **Dread:** Extreme anxiety in the face of a perceived or real threat.

Location and Felt Sense

Fear seems to be close to anger in my belly and solar plexus. It feels thick, leaden, heavy and massive, like sludge. It just sits there until it dissipates or I shift it. Fear and anger are closely related. An event evoking anger or fear can happen, but I deal with it and it's over and forgotten. A story I tell myself related to anger or fear is one I have to process over and over until I can let it go.

Fortunately, I've never been in a situation where I felt dread. I'm keeping my fingers crossed that I never will.

Here's one of my anger-fear events. When my car broke down on the highway a while ago, my first reaction was annoyance and frustration, as in, "Oh, _____! (Fill in your favorite swear word.) Why now? I don't need this. This _____ (fill in your next favorite one or two swear words) car!" On the heels of this reaction came insecurity, anxiety and alarm, as in, "No one's here to help me. I'm alone. How am I going to get out of this? It's probably going to cost a lot of money. _____ (Fill in your favorite string of swear words.)"

Of course, it all worked out. I calmed down, walked to the next exit, found a gas station, had my car towed, and the broken fan belt replaced. Once everything was taken care of, I exhaled and moved on. It was an anger-fear event that got fixed. Then I forgot about it until I pulled it out of my long-term memory bank for this chapter.

Here is one of my anger-fear stories. I have inherited a strong belief from the women in my family that independence and personal financial responsibility are important. If you are going to be in a relationship and commit to it, some issues, especially money, are non-negotiable. Of course, I've been tested on that many times and in many ways. One of the most memorable was in my second marriage.

We had agreed on how to handle our finances, but my husband frequently and consistently broke the rules. This led to discussions, which led to arguments, which led to a final angry outburst. I suddenly connected my anger to a deep-seated fear of financial failure that would surely end with me being broke, helpless and dependent.

It was only after recognizing that my anger was masking fear that I was I able to set financial boundaries for myself. This eased my anger toward my husband and my fear of not being in control of my own well-being. This was one of those never-ending fear patterns that could have shadowed me for years if I had not faced it, traced it, embraced it, and replaced it with self-awareness and a healthy behavioral response.

Was hubby okay with this? No, but that was his issue. I handled mine. He did not deal with it at any level. This was just one of many issues. *Sigh.*

Happiness
A sense of great pleasure and excitement.

Color
Sparkly white.

Shades

- **Kindness:** Being friendly, generous, considerate and compassionate.

- **Joy:** Well-being, anticipation, enjoyment and satisfaction.
- **Contentment:** Being accepting, calm and at peace with the way things are even if they cannot be changed.
- **Affection:** Attraction, fondness or tenderness toward something or someone.
- **Love:** A deep, strong feeling of wanting to connect and care for yourself, another or all humanity.

Location and Felt Sense

Chest, arms, neck and head. It feels like a Fourth of July sparkler that lights up quickly and slowly fades.

What makes me happy? Being in nature, especially in the mountains and forest. I am filled with contentment feeling the rhythm of my body walking on a forest path covered with pine needles, sitting on top of a mountain enjoying the vistas, taking in the fresh air, and happily eating chocolate, or feeling the warm spring sun on my shoulders as I walk from my house to the car.

Joy and contentment come up when I've completed a project and my work is appreciated. I'm working on being okay with just finishing it, but who doesn't like getting compliments, appreciation and acceptance? I want to be honest about my self-awareness journey and if I said I was totally content with just finishing something, I would not be telling you the truth.

The one last thing I want to say here is that happiness feels wonderful, but it is temporary. Contentment lasts a lot longer and, to me, is more serviceable for the long-term.

The other shade my palette knife stirs, moves around, and sorts through is love, the big Kahuna. To me, love is a verb that connotes tangible actions, like kindness, compassion and caring. I've become a bit wary and suspicious of people whose words of love easily drip off their tongues and spread like maple syrup on a stack of pancakes.

The words sound sincere and real, but when it's time for action, I have seen minds and behinds disappear, literally and figuratively.

I have not been lucky in love. However, I take full responsibility for my part in my relationship disasters. I was (please read the word "was" loud and clear) the good girl, who became an enabler in most of my relationships. That means I did my best to give the other person whatever they wanted or needed so I could earn my love fix. It was how I understood relationships, but that is not the way healthy relationships work.

Do I know better now? Yes, I do. Any relationship, love or otherwise, I enter into now is based on healthy boundaries. You do you and I do me, and let's meet somewhere in the middle. Sometimes it means I cross the middle to you, or you cross to me. That's being realistic. Life is like that.

It took some time and a lot of work for me to get to this point. Fortunately, I no longer engage in one-sided relationships and, as a result, I have many more contented, peaceful moments in life with groups, with individuals, or in solitude.

Sadness

Emotional pain from feelings of disadvantage, helplessness, disappointment or sorrow.

Color

Blue to dark gray.

Shades

- **The Blues:** Feeling unhappy, discontented, dejected, downcast or miserable.
- **Distress:** Experiencing acute mental or physical suffering.
- **Depression:** Living with persistent sadness, dejection, shame, guilt or loss of mental and physical vitality.

- **Grief:** Suffering an overwhelming sadness stemming from the loss of a loved one, a job, a personal disappointment or a devastating medical diagnosis.
- **Despair:** Experiencing hopelessness, futility or defeat.

Location and Felt Sense

A heavy sensation in the shoulders, chest and heart. It feels like I am carrying the weight of the world on my upper body.

I have not experienced prolonged grief. However, I know if my child, who is now a grown man, should die, I would be devastated. I don't think a parent ever gets over something like that. Maybe the sharp edge of grief dulls a bit with time, but I can't imagine it would ever totally disappear.

Sadness, on the other hand, is an emotion with which I am on speaking terms. I am sad when I get the news that a family member or friend has died because I miss them and appreciate what they have added to my life. Sometimes I'm sad and I don't know why. My house is clean. My bills are paid. I'm healthy and connected to my work, hobbies, friends and family. But despite it all, I feel sad.

Sadness in the form of the blues visits a bit more often than I would like, but so far I have been able to manage it. In my younger days, when the blues hit, I would take three mental health days. I would stay in bed, drink tea, eat toast, read or binge-watch television. At the end of three days without a bath or shower, when I couldn't stand myself anymore (I was single in those days, so it was just me), I'd get out of bed, take a shower, eat a healthy breakfast, and go back to work. The blues faded away. Now, I don't have to take mental health days. I use the tools in my self-awareness toolbox to figure out what is going on. I take action even if I can't figure it out. The blues eventually go away until the next time, and there always seems to be a next time.

Are my emotions real and useful? Yes! The assumption that someone who is practicing to enlighten up should be able to suppress or eliminate their emotions, live in everlasting bliss, and face every situation with equanimity is unrealistic. Having and feeling emotions in all their shades is a natural part of life.

Emotions are tools of the mind. They are neither positive nor negative. They just are. It's how we acknowledge, understand, manage and express them that make them helpful or unhelpful. I learned this the hard way over years of being told I was too emotional. This typically came from men (bosses and husbands) and, more often than not, when I was expressing clearly and directly how I was feeling and what I needed and wanted.

The next question becomes how to acknowledge, understand, manage and express our emotions in helpful and healing ways. Once we identify the colors on our emotional palette, we use the metaphorical knife to deconstruct, understand and accept what we're feeling and why. Then we use the metaphorical brush to paint appropriate responses.

Practice: The Triple-A Club
Quality to Embody: Acceptance

To DECONSTRUCT YOUR EMOTIONAL PALETTE, I recommend you take out a lifetime membership in the Triple-A Club. There are no dues, no meetings, no products and no rules. Simply try the following technique and, if it works for you, it's yours for life. If it doesn't, search until you find one that does.

The triple A's are:

1. Acknowledge
2. Accept
3. Act

Acknowledge

Learn to become aware of your mind-space and your emotional palette.

Acknowledging and naming your emotions in whatever form they present themselves to you is the first step to figuring out where they show up in your body, what triggers them, and what your mind thinks and feels about them.

Accept

- Accept that your emotions are real. They are part and parcel of what paints your worldview and your reactions or responses to what happens in your life.

- Accept that your emotions are yours. They are legitimate, and you have a right to acknowledge and experience them, no matter what anyone else says.

- Accept that you, and you alone, are responsible to find ways to manage the colors of your emotional palette in wise and balanced ways at any given moment.

Act

When something triggers you and you need to address it, acknowledge and name what you're feeling, accept that it is whatever it is, then take skillful action. A television commercial about quitting smoking says, "Every great why needs a great how." We've covered the *why*. Here are some *hows*.

Anger and Fear

Catch anger and fear simmering and bubbling before they boil and try this breathing technique.

1. Inhale for the count of three.
2. Hold your breath for the count of three.

3. Exhale slowly.

4. Repeat this for a minute or two or as long as you are comfortable.

Happiness

When you feel happy or excited, enjoy it. Smile and dance as though no one is watching. And if someone is watching, dance anyway!

Sadness

Try moving. Research shows movement is an excellent antidote for when the blues, in any shade, pay a visit. Take a walk, visit the gym, or try some gentle yoga. Movement offers the illusion of control, which may be enough to gain some respite for sadness. If you have a hobby or a craft, set aside time to work on it.

If you find healing through journaling, fill in the blanks in the following sentences as you move through the following mental actions:

- **Witness:** Identify the emotion/feeling and what may have brought it on.

  I am _____ (fill in an emotion/feeling) because _____ (fill in a situation or experience).

- **Reflect:** Identify the emotion/feeling and what may have brought it on in the past.

  I felt _____ (fill in an emotion/feeling) when _____ (fill in a situation or experience).

- **Dissect:** Check to see if the emotions are layered. Two or more of them may be playing out at the same time.

  When I feel _____ (fill in an emotion/feeling), I also feel _____ (fill in one or more emotion or feeling).

- **Detect:** Identify bodily sensations that are part of what you are experiencing and feeling. With practice, you'll be able to do this even during a strong emotional moment. All it takes is the acknowledgment that your emotional stew is simmering, bubbling or boiling.

You can use these techniques to manage emotions and feelings that need to be brought into balance.

In the end, the more comfortable you become with your emotional palette, its shades and layers, the more you will develop ways to acknowledge, accept and act appropriately to express them.

Never let your emotions rule, but always let them testify.

— Robert Brault

THE SKY IS BLUE,
BUT WHY ARE YOU?

*It's not the load that breaks you down,
it's the way you carry it.*

— Lena Horne

Here's the situation. You wake up one morning and feel the weight of the world on your shoulders. Or at some point during the day, your energy and mental state plummet into your personal well of despair. You feel heavy, sluggish and stuck in the mud of inaction. Every item on your to-do list feels impossible. The items on your must-do list feel formidable. And the things on your must-have-done-to-you list, like keeping doctors' appointments, getting your boobs mashed for your yearly mammogram, or bending over for your yearly proctology appointment, seem insurmountable. You feel like Sisyphus, the legendary king of Ephyra, condemned to eternally push a rock up the hill in Hades (that's a nice word for hell), only to have it roll down the hill repeatedly each time it nears the top. Life seems pointless. Why bother getting out of bed?

You are not alone. It happens to all of us. Sometimes despite getting a good night's sleep and eating healthy 90 percent of the time (we all need a few cheat days), we feel tired, irritated and mentally fogged, sad or restless. Maybe our digestion is off and while driving we feel road irritation. (Thankfully, many degrees away from road rage.) When this happens, many of us just want the day to be over so we can plop on the sofa, play games on one or more of our devices, read a book, eat chocolate, or catch up on TV shows. We just want to "chill" and check out.

To be clear, I am not talking about chronic grief or depression. I'm talking about the garden variety, out of nowhere, come and go blues. Why are they called "the blues" you ask? No one knows how the blues got that name or why the color blue became associated with feeling sad and poopy. This condition is also known by many other names, such as:

- Down in the mouth – a smile turned upside down.
- Bummed out – a hollow empty feeling.
- Down in the dumps – being stuck in your mental junkyard.
- Blue funk – a dark blue cloud surrounds you, rendering you invisible to, and isolated from, everyone else in the world.
- The ugly blues – cursing, crying, snot-nosed, can't-get-out-of-bed blues.

The blues, regardless of what we call them, are a normal part of our lives. Dozens of songs in pop culture have been written about the "blues." Here are just a few.

• Am I Blue?	• Down Home Blues
• Blue Monday	• A Mess of Blues
• Still Got the Blues	• Singing the Blues
• Rock Bottom Blues	• Lonesome Road Blues
• Bluer Than Blue	• Born to Be Blue

I even wrote a song about the blues. It's the first and only song I ever wrote, and the lyrics won honorable mention in a songwriting contest so long ago that I had forgotten about it until I mentioned to my son that I was searching for songs about the "blues."

He grinned and said, "I seem to remember a song called, 'The Brick Wall Blues.'"

After laughing and thanking him for remembering, I dug through my old files and found it. Here it goes.

The Brick Wall Blues

When things don't go the way they're planned
And there ain't no good news,
Say "hi" to them ol' irritatin'
Up against the brick wall blues.

When life becomes a mystery
And you ain't got no clues
You know you got them tribulatin'
Up against the brick wall blues.

Brick wall blues, brick wall blues
You try to win but always lose
You spend your life just payin' dues
And fightin' off those brick wall blues

When the hand that fortune deals you
Is not what you would choose
Say "hi" to them ol' aggravatin'
Up against the brick wall blues.

When your baby says it's over
'Cause you blew all your cues
You know you got them desolatin'
Up against the brick wall blues.

Brick wall blues, brick wall blues
You try to win but always lose
You spend your life just payin' dues
And fightin' off those brick wall blues

When age is creepin' up on you
And good times, they get fewer
When nothin' that you try will keep
Your blues from gettin' bluer

Try a little of this advice folks
It's really nothin' new
Just hang onto your self-respect
And you can break right through

Those brick wall blues, brick wall blues
You try to win but always lose
You spend your life just payin' dues
And fightin' off those brick wall blues

Those aggravatin' so frustratin'
Desolatin', irritatin'
Stomped down, trod on, tribulatin'
Up against a brick wall
Up against a brick wall
Up against the brick wall blues.

The blues are a common experience we all share regardless of who we are, where we are, or how we live. Even so, my blues will not look or feel like your blues. At this point in my life, I've gotten pretty good at catching the blues when they rise up. How? I use a blues jar. It's a mental image I've created for myself. Where do I keep it? I'd say deep in the lower right side of the back of my head. It's a clear glass mason jar with measures on the side ranging from one-quarter to a full eight-ounce cup.

I even know the source of this image. When I was a little girl, I used to play at my Aunt Lucy's house after school until my mom came home from work. Aunt Lucy had a room in the basement for the food she canned every year. The shelves were packed with rows of mason jars filled with colorful fruits and vegetables: tomatoes, peaches, cucumbers, rhubarb and string beans. The room had windows so the sun shone in and made the jars sparkle. That memory still brings me comfort, and the image of my blues jar helps keep my spirit fed in much the same way that Aunt Lucy's fruits and veggies filled my tummy at Sunday dinners.

This is how I work the image. When I check in, I envision myself within the mason jar. I look to see where my body is in relation to the measures marked on the side so I can assess the intensity of what I'm feeling. It's like the glass half-empty or half-full image.

When I'm feeling balanced, I see myself at the top—arms hanging over the edge, breathing in good energy, and grinning. Those are the light and sparkle days. When I'm out of sorts and see myself at the three-quarter mark, it's a down in the mouth day. At the halfway mark, I'm bummed out. At the one-third mark, I'm down in the dumps. At the one-quarter mark, it's a serious blue funk. When slumped at rock bottom, it's the ugly blues and I'm in my personal well of despair. It's full of broken dreams, sorrow stones, weeping weeds, sleepless slime, muddy moods, and all kinds of subconscious nasties and demons. Those are bad days.

But sometimes, when I'm at the bottom and start sifting through the muck, I find a thread of awareness that has been eluding me. When I trace it to the source, I often get a glimpse into why I'm feeling blue and a clue to how I can pull myself out of the muck and up to the top.

I've discovered that when my blues appear, it's usually because of one of three things. First, I'm doing too much and the blues slow me down to make me take a break and rest. Second, there is a creative impulse, change or life lesson that needs to come up and out for processing. And third, it might be that I'm slogging through my annual post-holiday, gray sky, seasonal affective disorderly blahs. Yes, I know the technical term is seasonal affective disorder, but it feels downright disorderly to me.

I recently had a case of the blues about my work teaching, writing and volunteering. It felt mundane, obligatory and repetitive. I was in denial since facing my feelings would mean saying "no" to something I'd happily said "yes" to earlier and disappointing others. As a recovering perfectionist, that is difficult to do. Getting to that glimpse of "why" allowed me to acknowledge my denial and open my mind to a needed change.

This meant simplifying and re-aligning my schedule. Once I enlightened up and accepted it, the blues lifted and I made the necessary changes. Did you read what I wrote? I accepted it and the blues lifted. Then I made the necessary changes. It's the acceptance that triggers the lifting of the blues, not having to make changes first, at least for me. Getting to "yes" means it's okay to say "yes" to me and "no" to others so I can keep myself balanced physically, mentally and emotionally. What a concept!

Practice: Three Tips to Manage the Blues
Quality to Embody: Understanding

IS THERE A DIFFERENCE BETWEEN KNOWING and understanding? Yes, there is. Knowing means you have a basic awareness of your blues when they visit—the what. Understanding means you've taken time to reflect and deepen that awareness to gain in-depth insight into the reasons they dropped in for a visit—the why.

Here are three tips for managing the blues when they come.

1. Observe yourself.
2. Move.
3. Raise your energy.

Observe Yourself

Once you know you're dealing with the blues, try to observe the effect they are having on you. This checklist may be helpful.

- **Observe your body:** Are you experiencing something physical that has you down in the dumps, like a pulled muscle, headache, constipation, digestive upset and so on?

- **Observe your breath:** Are you breathing deeply or is your breath shallow, quick and stuck in your throat or chest?

- **Observe your energy level:** Use a scale of one to ten to rate your energy level, with one being "I'm toast, just bury me now!" and ten being "Where's the party?"

- **Observe your mental state:** Why are you feeling blue, unbalanced, freaked out, anxious, disconnected or out of sorts? Is there an issue or life lesson you need to address or change? What has come up to come out?

Sometimes you'll get an answer and sometimes you won't. The important step in the process is to ask these questions to gain a measure of self-awareness or to accept that it is eluding you at the moment. That's okay too, as long as you observe and recognize it.

Next question: Do you want to wait out the blues or take action and shift your mood? If the blues are temporary and don't linger (you can decide how long that is for you), you can choose to sit with them until they pass on their own, or you can take action and shift your energy until you feel lighter, stable and balanced.

Move!

This is especially important if the blues make your body and mind feel heavy, sluggish and stuck. Go for a walk, punch the air, stamp your feet, or do some type of exercise. Move in a way that creates heat and encourages action. Research has shown movement can help you shift the blues.

Try shaking it off. This exercise is typically done standing but can be easily done seated in a chair. Shake It Off will energize your body, increase oxygen levels in the bloodstream, stimulate your nervous system, and help with mental focus. Just what you need to give blues the boot.

INSTRUCTIONS

1. Stand with your feet about shoulder-width apart.
2. Bend your knees slightly and begin to shake your legs.
3. Move the vibration up into your torso.
4. Next, shake your wrists and move the shaking up your arms to your shoulders.
5. Invite your head to join the party if that feels comfortable.
6. Feel free to raise your arms or bend forward or backward.
7. Shake your body for three to five minutes (or more) a few times a day.
8. When done, simply stand or sit quietly.
9. Feel the effects of shaking your body and shifting your energy.

Raise Your Energy

One way to raise your energy is to use the Gesture of the Inner Smile, an exercise for cultivating a feeling of lightness. It is called "Hansi mudra" in the yoga tradition and is helpful when your spirits need a lift.

INSTRUCTIONS

1. Touch the tips of your index, middle and ring fingers to the thumb on each hand.
2. Extend your pinky finger straight out.

3. Rest the backs of your hands on your thighs or knees, or you can raise your hands out to the sides of your body with the pinky fingers pointing upward.

4. Relax your shoulders and keep your spine comfortably aligned.

5. Breathe naturally.

6. Hold this pose for two to five minutes, or longer if you are comfortable.

I think a good quote is like a poem. It gives you the essence of what you are trying to say and does it in just a few words. Here's one that fits the blues.

> *You cannot prevent the birds of sorrow from flying over your head, but you can prevent them from building nests in your hair.*

— Chinese proverb

When the birds of sorrow land, use your blues tips to make sure they don't build nests and move in.

BITCHCRAFT

It took me quite a long time to develop a voice, and now that I have it, I am not going to be silent.

— Madeleine Albright

M y son gave me the title for this chapter. We were celebrating his birthday with dinner at a local Chinese restaurant and catching each other up on our creative projects. He's a graphic artist and a musician. I told him I was working on an chapter that explored the word "bitch," how it is applied to women, how women apply the word to themselves, and how we could use its power to navigate a world loaded with "-isms" (sexism, racism, ageism, liberalism, conservatism, nativism, populism, etc.). I was going to call it, "The Bitch Has a Voice."

That idea came to me last spring when I walked into my local library and passed a display of new books. One title caught my eye. *The Bitch is Back.* I yanked it off the shelf, checked it out, and devoured it. Then I went back for the earlier book, *The Bitch in the House.* I devoured that one too. I was, as they say, "on fire" with the idea.

Each book is a collection of chapters edited by Cathi Hanauer. They illuminate the lives of a diverse group of women who wrote about their struggles, successes, self-perceptions, and how they navigated their place in the world.

After telling my son about it, he suggested I consider "Bitchcraft" as the title of this chapter. I loved it because the word "craft" is defined as an art, trade or occupation that requires a special skill. Using Bitchcraft to navigate a world loaded with "-isms" requires considerable skill and self-awareness.

The original definition of "bitch" is a female dog. To a patriarchal misogynist, it means a woman who is unreasonable, malicious, belligerent, spiteful, bossy, overbearing or aggressive. In a feminist context, it means a strong and assertive woman. In RuPaul's *Drag Race Dictionary*, bitch means a fierce woman and is used as a term of endearment among drag queens. Gloria Steinem, the feminist activist, has given women a crafty way to respond when the B-word is tossed our way, "The best thing I've thought of to say when someone calls you a bitch is, 'Thank you.'"

That's a great response when one is called a bitch, but when a woman is objectified, ignored, devalued or disrespected and responds with anger, resistance or pushback, she is often seen as a bitch even if no one utters the word.

The "craft" in Bitchcraft is knowing how to manage the anger, how to push back, and make your point in an authentic, conscious voice delivered without apology. To do that, we need to understand the three stages of Bitchcraft.

- **Stage 1:** Quiet fuming, stuffing and repressing reactions to being objectified, ignored, devalued or disrespected.
- **Stage 2:** Raw snarky, shoot-from-the-hip reactions.
- **Stage 3:** Sassy, self-aware, assertive, appropriate, authentic, responses and actions delivered without apology.

My journey toward Stage 3 has taken many years with several steps forward and more than a few steps back.

In my younger days, my one-note reaction to being ignored, insulted, objectified or treated as "less than" was anger, but I'd stuff, repress or control it to present myself as the good girl I'd been trained to be. That is pure Stage 1.

During my freshman year at college, my English professor asked us to write a report on our favorite work of literature—something of meaning that is considered to have lasting importance. I did mine on *Little Women* by Louisa May Alcott. It was my favorite because of Jo, the young woman with a hot temper who was less interested in learning "womanly ways" and more interested in exploring her own interests, which were reading, writing and her individuality. I so related to Jo. I wrote and submitted my paper.

A few days later the professor gave us feedback. He said something I've never forgotten. "Someone in this class actually thinks that *Little Women* is literature." Then he laughed. I was mortified and infuriated. Didn't he know *Little Women* had been, and still is, one of the most iconic books in American literary history? Was he dismissing it because a woman wrote it? At the time, I did not have the language, self-awareness or self-confidence to challenge or protest, so I stuffed my anger and seethed in silence.

The stuffing and repressing led to a whole heap of stress-related problems, like headaches, colds, rashes, stomachaches and constipation. When being a "good girl" got to be a real drag, something had to give. When I finally found my voice and used it, it was raw, snarky and held nothing back.

One of those moments came while I was working at a local television station. My job was to produce local "talking head" shows and public service documentaries. I was having a problem working with some of the male production staff. Was it because I was Black, a woman, a young twenty-something, or all of those? I didn't know, but in an effort to straighten out the problem, I went to talk to the production director.

When I walked into his office, he was chatting with the news director. I was admittedly a bit hot under the collar, but I was not rude. I asked for help to get the support I needed to do my job. He shrugged me off and, as I turned to leave, I heard him say to the news director, "What a bitch!"

I turned back and without missing a beat, let loose with, "Maybe I am a bitch, but I'm a good bitch. I've worked long and hard because I care about what I do and, if that makes me a bitch in your minds, so be it!"

I watched their mouths drop open. I stormed out of the office, still pissed but satisfied because I gave as good as I got.

Was I unreasonable, belligerent and bossy or righteously angry, authentic and standing up for myself? That depends on who you ask, but if I was going to be seen as a bitch, then I was going to be the best bitch possible in the feminist meaning of the word. That's when I took the power of the word back and internalized it. It was Stage 2. It felt good, but it wasn't full Bitchcraft.

It was easier to practice my new Bitchcraft skills in the workplace. After all, my co-workers weren't family or best friends, and I didn't go home to them at the end of the day. My personal life was another minefield I had to navigate my way through step-by-step to inch my Bitchcraft closer to Stage 3, the master level.

For some reason, or maybe several reasons, I've failed at being married, twice. Maybe I chose poorly. Back then, like a little puppy, I trusted anyone who paid attention to me. Yes, I was naïve and dependent on others to feel okay. Yes, I was, at the same time, stubborn and outspoken about what I saw as right or wrong. Yes, I was a co-dependent perfectionist who felt it was my responsibility to make things right. Yes, I hadn't dealt with the ways in which I was not perfect and was, in fact, broken in a lot of places. And yes, I was (and still am) a work in progress. It's complicated.

My first marriage was fairly typical. It started with passion and optimism right up to the time I began to question the traditional wife-mother role I was living in the early 1970s. We both worked, but I did most of the housework, childcare, cooking and cleaning. My efforts to discuss this were met with laughter or silence. I was ignored. Then I got involved in community work, helping with voter registration. Why did I add one more thing to my list? It was a distraction from the growing unhappiness with my life and my inability to figure this "marriage thing" out.

It came to a head one day as I got into my car to attend a meeting. The passenger side door opened and my husband pointed his shotgun at me. My reaction? Full force eruption. Raw anger flared up. The inner bitch roared. I stared him down and dared him to pull the trigger. WTF?! I look back at that now and wonder what the hell was I thinking? Probably, I wasn't. I was reacting. I often wonder what he was thinking. I don't have a clue. We were divorced soon after.

My second marriage was basically a repeat of the first because I had not yet learned to be self-aware, assertive and authentically me. I didn't know when or how to appropriately stand my ground or give some up. This man's weapons were words. According to him, I was failing at my wifely responsibilities.

- "You're too emotional."
- "You read too much."
- "You think too much."
- "You don't know how to love."

Etcetera, etcetera, etcetera, and on and on and on. I retreated into Stage 1 with silent fuming, stuffing and repressing.

One day, I was deep into work on my master's thesis, and yes, I still needed an outside distraction because I did not know how to handle what was happening in my relationship. I didn't know if the failure was mine, his or a sad mix of both. But this time when he interrupted my study time for the same litany of complaints, something snapped inside my head. I was not going to stuff, placate or try to explain myself one more time. I'd hit bottom. I gave up. I looked him in the eye and said, "You're right and, if I'm all those things you say, then I don't understand why you are still here and married to me. Maybe you need to find someone else."

His response was shocked silence and retreat. My Bitchcraft had reached Stage 2, but I still didn't know how to navigate the marriage or figure out when and how to leave.

That brings me to the present. After a lot of self-reflection and a couple of good therapists, I alternate between Stages 2 and 3. I use every bit of my hard-won self-awareness to pick and choose relationships wisely, to look before I leap into a situation. I say "no" to toxic people and situations with as much compassion and kindness as I can muster. This, plus growing older and wiser, has drastically cut down the number and type of situations that call for Bitchcraft. When they do happen, I can take a step back, assess the situation, and respond more often at Stage 3.

For example, I was a member of a professional organization for writers and publishers. When I first joined, we participated in a variety of craft fairs to sell our books. The person who arranged them was drill-sergeant efficient and the events went off without a hitch.

Then came a glitch. I misread the instructions for an event and brought the wrong size table. The people I shared the space with helped me place the table so it fit and did not encroach on anyone else's space. The organizer came over and made an issue about it. I calmly and politely explained what had happened and how as a group, we had solved the problem (Stage 3 Bitchcraft).

The next day the organizer posted on the group's Facebook page and made a bigger issue of the incident. I took a deep breath, posted back to the group, and apologized for any inconvenience my mistake had caused. The organizer then sent me a personal email castigating me yet again for my mistake and my response to her. She copied the organization's president on the message. I was furious, and my fingers itched to respond at Bitchcraft Stage 2.

I wisely put that urge on hold. Since I had explained my error to the organizer and apologized to the group, I did not want to engage in any further back and forth. I hit the delete button.

Later that day, I received an apology from the president on behalf of the organization. I used my best Stage 3 Bitchcraft to explain I did not understand the organizer's reaction to the situation or to me. It felt personal and I felt disrespected. A few hours afterward, the organizer announced on Facebook that she would no longer organize our events. A few days later, she quit the group. Clearly, there was more going on, and I had been caught in the middle of her muddle. Her people skills were sadly lacking, but she was damn good at her job, and those skills would be missed. On the upside, I had practiced Stage 3 Bitchcraft.

Practice: The SASSY Bill of Rights and Responsibilities

Quality to Embody: Assertiveness

STAGE 3 BITCHCRAFT NEEDS REGULAR PRACTICE. SASSY is an assertiveness technique to help you use your Stage 3 Bitchcraft skills more often.

Definitions of "sassy" range from impudent and cheeky to lively, bold, stylish, full of spirit, distinctively smart, and possessing an amazing amount of cool. A sassy person exhibits **S**trength,

Authenticity, **S**kill, **S**erenity and is **Y**oung-at-heart. They can also express these qualities in all areas of life.

Each of the rights and responsibilities that follow contains a tip or technique to practice. Pick any one to start and add in others at your own pace.

Be Strong

Your Right: I have the right to be here, to be safe, and to stand my ground.

In Bitchcraft Stage 1, it can be hard to find your voice and express yourself assertively and confidently. To move forward, it is crucial to master this skill. First, recognize that you may be stuffing your feelings, your needs, and your truth. As you unstuff, you will find healthy ways to stand your ground.

Your Responsibility: I have a responsibility to be disciplined in my growth process while I practice compassion with others.

Roots Visualization

This can be especially helpful in tense situations. It calms Bitchcraft Stages 1 and 2, and fertilizes the ground for Stage 3. Try to practice this when you are not in the middle of a difficult situation. That way, it's "top of mind" when you need it.

To practice when you are not in a difficult situation, take off your shoes, connect your bare feet to the ground, and close your eyes. It's even better if you can do this outdoors with your feet in the grass, dirt or sand.

When ready, visualize your body growing roots, starting from the base of the spine, that reach down through your legs to the bottoms of your feet, and from the bottoms of your feet through the earth's crust. Visualize your roots branching and spreading, growing stronger and reaching deeper into the earth's core. Feel the strength, support and stability your branching roots give you.

Sense this connection and, as you breathe, begin to draw in strength, support and stability through your roots. Allow a sense of safety, security, stability and connection to the physical world and your place in it to fill your entire being. Draw these qualities through the bones of your feet and legs to the base of your spine and up to the crown of your head. Feel your entire body to be safe, secure, stable and connected to the physical world so you can stand your ground and speak your truth.

You may feel some tingling or pulsing in your feet and legs. That's a good thing. After all, energy flows where intention goes. You can shorten or lengthen the visualization to accommodate the time you have. The most important point is to attune yourself physically, mentally and emotionally to what you need at that moment to stand your ground assertively, appropriately and confidently.

Of course, if you find yourself in a situation, you probably won't be able to take off your shoes or close your eyes. In that case, turn your internal attention to your feet and feel the weight of your body pressing into the soles of your feet as the connection between your feet and earth deepens.

Be Assertive

Your Right: I have the right to express my thoughts, feelings, wants and needs in honest and appropriate ways.

When you are being assertive, it's easier to practice Bitchcraft at the master level. However, there are always circumstances where being assertive is difficult, not advisable or even possible, and you find yourself reverting to Bitchcraft Stages 1 or 2. Do your best and persevere.

Your Responsibility: I have a responsibility to respect the thoughts, feelings, wants and needs of others.

Cultivating Self-Esteem

The Gesture of Self-Esteem is an exercise that cultivates self-esteem, determinism and self-mastery. It is called "Brahma mudra" in the yoga tradition and is helpful when you need those qualities to practice assertive Stage 3 Bitchcraft.

INSTRUCTIONS

1. Hold your hands in front of your body with your palms facing toward you.

2. Tuck your thumbs into the palms of your hands.

3. Close your fingers over your thumbs.

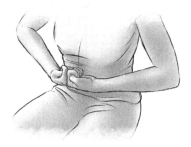

4. Place the fists together with the base of your fingers touching. Press them gently against each other with the fingernails facing up.

5. Rest the pinky-finger side of both hands against your body just above your belly button. Press lightly.

6. Hold your elbows away from the body.

7. Silently or aloud, say "I am cool, calm, confident and courageous."

8. Repeat the affirmation a minimum of nine times.

Be Skillful

Your Right: I have the right to healthy, mutually beneficial relationships, starting with my relationship with myself and my life.

Our ability to choose, engage and work with our relationships depends on developing a healthy relationship with ourselves first. Where we are in our self-awareness journey is often clearly reflected in how we practice Bitchcraft. Here is Kate's story.

I met Kate while traveling with a women-only group in Oaxaca, Mexico. You know how women share when we get down to the real nitty-gritty, right? One evening while drinking margaritas and chatting over dinner, the B-word came up.

One woman said she just didn't like to hear it or use it. Kate suggested she just "own it" and went on to tell us how, as a wife, mom and teacher, she spent most of her life doing for others. Once retired, she found herself at loose ends. One morning, she planted herself in front of the bathroom mirror and asked, "What would a selfish bitch do?"

That clicked everything in place and she declared it The Year of The Selfish Bitch. For a full year, she stood in front of that mirror every day and asked herself the same question. When she got an answer, she practiced skillful action and made herself a priority.

Your Responsibility: I have a responsibility to discriminate between actions motivated by strength and those motivated by anger and fear.

Take Skillful Action

This exercise will help you get in touch with a personal issue that may be affecting your relationship with yourself and how you function in relationship to others. Practicing it helps you analyze it and address it using skillful action.

1. **Face it:** State your issue, problem or situation silently or aloud. Try it in front of a mirror, like Kate did.

2. **Trace it:** Consider these questions:

   * Why is this an issue, situation or problem?
   * Is it new or has it been around for a while?

- Are my own thoughts, feelings, beliefs and actions contributing to it?
- If so, which ones?
- Are they helpful or unhelpful?
- How do I feel about this?

3. **Embrace it:** Welcome and witness any answers that float into your awareness. It often helps to write them down, record them, draw pictures, write or journal.

4. **Take skillful action:** What Stage 3 Bitchcraft skills can you employ to assertively address your issue or situation?

   - What do you need to say to yourself or someone else?
   - What one specific action can you take to move forward?
   - How assertive and authentic can you be?
   - How will you handle yourself if blocked in your efforts to be assertive and authentic?

Be Serene

Your Right: I have the right to all of my thoughts and emotions, including anger.

Accepting this as your right eases the discomfort you might feel when others tell you that you are being too emotional, loud or angry when you are trying to be assertive. Men are still rewarded more than women for being assertive. The key is to understand why you feel the way you do and then to use Stage 3 Bitchcraft to respond, even if you feel like crawling back into your she shed or tearing your tormentor "a new one."

Your Responsibility: I have a responsibility to manage my thoughts and emotions and use their power for balance, self-care and wisdom.

Release Attachment to Outcomes

Accepting that life takes unforeseen turns is one way to move through it with a degree of serenity. Regardless of what happens in your life and what actions you take or reactions or responses you make, there are only four outcomes to any experience or situation.

1. What you expected.
2. Less than you expected.
3. More than you expected.
4. The unexpected.

Once you accept that you may influence outcomes, but you do not control them, you'll find it becomes easier to release attachments to the results of your actions. When you do, it will be easier to slide into Stage 3 Bitchcraft, go with the flow, and respond to any situation with a measure of serenity.

Be Young-at-Heart

Your Right: I have the right to be vital and creative, and to eat ice cream for breakfast.

Ice cream for breakfast is perfectly fine as long as you do it consciously and in moderation. B. K. S. Iyengar agrees when he says:

> *In this way, we discover the ability to refuse ice cream or to accept it but in quantities that will not be harmful. We increasingly develop judicious discrimination that, harnessed to self-control, enables us to set sail in uncharted waters.*[24]

Your Responsibility: I have a responsibility to live as balanced, joyful and wise a life as possible.

---

24 B. K. S. Iyengar. *Light on Life: The Yoga Journey to Wholeness, Inner Peace, and Ultimate Freedom.* Rodale Books. Kindle edition.

Defy Stereotypes of Aging (at any age)

There are many ways to accomplish this. Here are a few suggestions.

1. Every month, on the date of your birth, celebrate by doing something you've never done before.
2. Laugh. Find out what tickles your funny bone and laugh several times a day.
3. Exercise. It's not an option. It's a necessity!
4. Keep your brain cells active. Learn a new skill.
5. Take up a new hobby.
6. Develop friendships with younger people.

And remember...

Assertiveness is not what you do, it's who you are!

— Shakti Gawain

Good luck honing your Bitchcraft skills!

Your Fourth Layer of Self-Awareness: Intuitive Wisdom

The Taittiriya Upanishad states that discrimination (wisdom or clarity) is the heart of working with this layer. We can view the fourth layer of self-awareness on many levels, from the mystical to the practical. Because this book focuses on the practical, we'll look at aspects of the witness we can employ daily to become aware of and reflect on our habits, beliefs and behaviors as we move through the ups and downs of our lives.

The witness, for our purposes, is often referred to as higher intelligence, insight, intuition or wisdom. It's the lamp of self-awareness that illuminates all aspects of ourselves for understanding, acceptance and integration. Self-awareness is developed and deepened by engaging and working with the witness. The goal is to become aware of and manage our unhelpful core beliefs, habits and behavior patterns until we are able to loosen and release their hold on us. Self-awareness at the level of the witness also helps us recognize, celebrate and share our creativity and talents.

The witness overlaps and shares space with the mind, our third layer of self-awareness. To visualize this, imagine two circles that overlap by 50 percent, like a Venn diagram. One circle is the mind and the other is the witness.

Here's an example that helps us understand how layered and interrelated they are and how they work together.

A core belief that "I'm not good enough" can exist in both the mind and the witness but at different

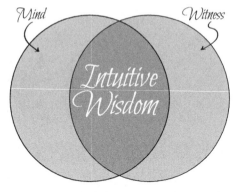

levels of awareness. In the Witness circle, "I'm not good enough" might be seen as messages of unworthiness from family, friends and society at large for any number of reasons, such as race, gender, gender identification, class, physical or mental ability. In the mind circle, "I'm not good enough" might be believed and expressed through depression, addictions and other self-sabotaging behaviors.

However, the witness, seeing where it comes from and knowing the core belief of "I'm not good enough" is not true, does its best to send that message to the mind through the overlapping space the two layers share. When the mind opens to receive the message, it may experience an *aha* moment of total understanding, or it may be able to acknowledge that the cause and source of the belief need to be examined. In either case, steps can be taken to make a choice for positive change, keep the status quo with full knowledge of the consequences, or find acceptance if change is not possible.

If you follow guidance from the witness, you will move toward the goal of wholeness on your self-awareness journey. The witness is an integral, inseparable, indispensable part of your being—a true and deep part that leads you, if you are willing to listen, toward clarity, contentment and resilience.

The goal of working with this layer is to bring about physical, mental and emotional awareness, to acknowledge both non-productive habit patterns, along with positive traits and talents. Most of us begin the process of engaging the witness through our everyday intelligence. It's a starting point. Then gradually, with consistent practice, the mind is able to open more frequently to intuition, wisdom or *aha* moments in which awareness, acceptance and understanding bloom.

When you regularly practice witnessing your thoughts, emotions, beliefs and behavior without judgment, you are better able to identify and understand where they come from and how and why they are impacting your life. When the witness is awake, especially in real-time, you will see your reality as it is, not hidden behind a veil of wishful thinking, denial or delusion. As a result, you can consciously choose your path forward with full awareness of the potential consequences.

When the light of wisdom and understanding shines, you will be able to accept yourself as you are without judgment, consciously change a habit, replace an unhelpful thought pattern with a constructive one, or change an emotional reaction into a productive response. This process results in increased calm and resilience in the way you face the events of your life.

Witnessing is a two-level process.

Sometimes witnessing occurs in the present moment. This enables you to hit pause in the space between what is happening and how you might respond. All too often, the pause is not seen or sensed and the resulting action is impulsive.

Sometimes witnessing occurs with reflection. You may choose to face what is happening in your life that causes anxiety, concern or difficulty. Or you may reflect on the past to catch a glimpse of where it comes from and why it's impacting your life.

If you are like most people, you will take one step forward and two steps back on your journey. This will happen repeatedly. Remember, it's a process—sometimes painful and sometimes joyful but worth doing because of the peace of mind and level of conscious living it can bring you.

A key strategy for engaging the witness is the ability to pay attention. To sharpen that skill, we turn to steps five and six of the Nine Steps to Self-Awareness. These two steps ask us to first turn the mind back on itself, then take skillful action.

Step 5. Turn the Mind Back on Itself

OUR PURPOSE IS TO UNCOVER THE source and intention of our beliefs. To do that, we might ask ourselves:

- How long have I believed this?
- Why do I believe it?
- Where did this belief come from?
- What hold does it have on me?
- How is it impacting my life?
- Is this belief making my situation more difficult?
- Does this belief help me move toward clarity, contentment and resilience?
- Do I need to accept it, transform it, or let this belief go?

The suggested practices for this step are conscious relaxation and meditation.

Conscious relaxation is deep relaxation with an inner awareness of body, breath and mind. Many techniques bring about conscious relaxation. Most start by focusing attention and awareness on the first three layers of self-awareness: physical, energetic and mental. Then, as comfort permits, attention and awareness are guided to the witness.

Research shows conscious relaxation fosters receptivity, learning and problem-solving. It enhances your ability to:

- become comfortable dealing with psycho-emotional material from the subconscious mind.
- develop willpower and the ability to concentrate.
- understand that you have feelings, but you are not your feelings. You are so much more.
- let go of unhelpful core beliefs, habits or patterns and replace them with positive helpful ones.
- observe your thoughts and emotions without getting caught up in them.
- consciously make changes, choose not to, or find peace of mind if change is not possible.

Conscious relaxation is not hypnosis. In hypnosis, the subject is led into a deep sleep where the brain completely shuts down. In conscious relaxation, the goal is to remain awake, which allows you to maintain a thread of consciousness well beyond the hypnogogic state. Conscious relaxation, unlike hypnosis, does not depend on suggestion and persuasion. In guided practices, the instructions are given directly, and the practitioner is reminded that they, not the instructor, are in charge of their experience. The instructor is a guide who gives the technique but does not force or compel the practitioner in any way.

In his book, *The Meditative Mind*, Daniel Goleman says:

> *Meditation is now a standard tool used in medicine, psychology, education and self-development. As these meditators have taken their places in the ranks of businesspeople, professionals and*

> *academics, they have made meditation a part of*
> *the fabric of the culture.*[25]

Meditation is not about trying or striving to achieve ecstasy, bliss or tranquility. It is the creation of a space in which we can observe and study our own mind. Some teachers say the goal of meditation is to control the mind. Perhaps some can do that, but most of us living lives in our material everyday world will do better by setting the more realistic goal to witness, understand and manage our thoughts, emotions, habits and behaviors.

The two basic paths of meditation practice are mindfulness and concentration. Mindfulness is considered to be more passive, and concentration more active. Both paths offer many techniques to choose from.

Mindfulness Meditation

Jon Kabat-Zinn, the founder of mindfulness-based stress reduction and author of *Full Catastrophe Living*, says:

> *Mindfulness is moment-to-moment awareness. It*
> *is a systematic approach to developing new kinds*
> *of control and wisdom in our lives, based on our*
> *inner capacities for relaxation, paying attention,*
> *awareness and insight.*[26]

In mindfulness meditation, you can think of the mind as a puppy on a long leash, allowing it to move freely, darting and dashing about, but with full awareness of what it is experiencing.

Concentration Meditation

Concentration meditation techniques work by channeling the mind's full attention into a single focus, such as a sound, a piece of

---

25   Daniel Goleman. *The Meditative Mind*. G. P. Putnam's Sons, New York, 1988.

26   Jon Kabat-Zinn. *Full Catastrophe Living*. Dell Publishing, New York, 1990.

music, breathing, a picture, an object or a physical position. The goal is to keep bringing one's attention back to the selected focus when the mind wanders. And the mind will wander. In concentration meditation, you can think of the mind as a puppy on a short leash.

Myths and Misconceptions about Meditation

When the suggestion is made to add a meditation practice to our lives, the response all too often is "I can't meditate," followed by any number of reasons, hindrances and objections. Here are a few examples and responses.

- **I can't sit in the lotus position.**

  Meditation can be done in any position as long as you can keep a comfortably straight spine and remain awake and aware.

- **I can't stop my thoughts.**

  Stopping your thoughts is not realistic. Depending on your chosen technique, the goal is to observe your thoughts without judgment.

- **I can't block out my feelings and memories.**

  Blocking feelings and memories is not realistic. The process of observing your feelings and memories will lead to a better understanding of them and how they impact your life.

- **I can't control my mind.**

  Most of us can't. The goal is to understand the mind and learn to manage your thoughts and emotions.

- **I can't afford the classes.**

  There are many sources of free information. Check your local library and search online.

- **I'm too busy.**

  Incorporate a technique in your life that works with your schedule. For instance, you might choose a walking meditation as you move from room-to-room in your home or from your home to your car or the bus station.

- **There are too many distractions in my house.**

  Distractions are part of the meditation process. When you notice a distraction, acknowledge it and return to the meditation technique you've chosen.

- **Meditation makes you passive, apathetic and unemotional.**

  Meditation makes you self-aware, discerning and peaceful.

- **Meditation is too hard.**

  Try a variety of techniques until you find one you can do comfortably.

- **Meditation is a selfish activity.**

  Self-care is not selfish. Meditation is an activity that fosters self-care, which in turn can result in you being kinder and more giving to others.

- **Meditation is prayer.**

  Meditation is different than prayer. It is a set of techniques that encourage a heightened state of awareness that has been shown to have a wide number of benefits to both the mind and body.

It's important to understand the difference between practicing meditation and experiencing a meditative state. They are often spoken about as if they are the same thing. They are not. To practice meditation, you select a technique, a length of time, and commit to practice. The self-discipline needed to accomplish this is under your control.

Meditative states are another thing altogether. They are not under your control. You choose to practice, but the states may or may not choose you. You can practice and witness what happens, but you need to release any attachment to the results of your practice.

No matter the meditation practice you choose, the meditative state will happen or it won't. When you understand that meditation is a journey and not a destination, you learn to:

- maintain stillness or awareness of conscious movement (for example, walking).
- achieve relaxed breathing.
- consciously relax the body.
- calmly observe the mind.

The benefits are many. Here are some science-based benefits of meditation. Meditation:

- reduces stress.
- reduces symptoms of anxiety.
- promotes emotional health.
- enhances self-awareness.
- lengthens attention span.
- may reduce age-related memory loss.
- can generate kindness.
- may help fight addictions.
- improves sleep.
- helps manage pain.
- can decrease blood pressure.
- can be performed anywhere.

Here is a list of additional benefits reported by many students. Meditation:

- helps keep things in perspective.
- increases peace of mind.
- helps you live more authentically.
- increases compassion and decreases judgment of self and others.
- deepens understanding of yourself and others.
- increases acceptance of oneself, warts and all.
- helps with the work of forgiveness.
- helps with seeing things as they really are.

If conscious relaxation and meditation reduce stress, as the research suggests they do, then that can help us live our lives with more clarity, contentment and resilience.

Step 6. Take Skillful Action

HERE WE EMPLOY THE RESULTS AND learnings from our practice of conscious relaxation and meditation to take skillful action and make choices that bring balance to our lives. When we can productively solve problems, clear obstacles, and address our issues or situations, we can have a direct experience of clarity and contentment. We will be more resilient and stress hardy.

The recommendation for this step is to select a conscious relaxation or meditation technique you can commit to and that fits into your life. What you choose and when, where and how long you practice is completely up to you.

As you begin to take all this in, remember the mind has a tendency to sleepwalk through daily life, but the witness is always awake. When you open and tune into this aspect of your consciousness, there is a coming together, a balance and an integration of both the witness and mind that results in a deep sense of peace. B. K. S. Iyengar puts it this way:

> *A stable mind is like the hub of a wheel. The world may spin around you, but the mind is steady.*[27]

With practice, you can engage your witness, bring clear, focused attention to what you find, and accept all aspects of yourself, pleasant and not so pleasant. When you listen to the whisperings of the witness, you will spend less time sleepwalking through your life on autopilot. You will step forth into it with clarity, contentment and resilience.

The following chapters explore additional perspectives on the witness and share personal stories about waking the witness, living in a complicated world, how to make conscious choices, and how to work with our "shadow" side. The suggested practices are designed to help you enhance the qualities of observation, courage, equanimity and gratitude.

---

27 B. K. S. Iyengar. *Light on Life: The Yoga Journey to Wholeness, Inner Peace, and Ultimate Freedom.* Rodale Books. Kindle edition.

CAN I GET A WITNESS?

As you become more clear about who you
really are, you'll be better able to decide what
is best for you—the first time around.

— Oprah Winfrey

The answer to the question "Can I get a witness?" is... you already have one. Your mission, should you choose to accept it (and I hope you do), is to wake your witness, engage it, and let it help you to become clear about who you really are and what you need to do to find clarity, contentment and resilience in our complicated world.

This mission is not impossible. Let's start with the definition of "witness."

Knowledge, testimony; an attesting of a fact,
statement; to be present at, to see personally; to
give or serve as evidence; to testify to religious
beliefs or faith—to bear witness.

We can look at the word and its meanings through many other lenses: secular, religious, philosophical, psychological and spiritual.

Through the secular lens, we think of the legal setting. When we hear the word "witness," we generally think of a person swearing under oath to give truthful evidence in a court about what they know or saw.

Through the religious lens, we learn that the question "Can I get a witness?" goes back to the 19th-century African American church tradition. It is still used as a call and response where a parishioner or minister, after sharing a personal experience, seeks affirmation by asking, "Can I get a witness?" to which the congregation replies "Amen!" offering acknowledgment and acceptance to the speaker and the message.

Through the philosophical, psychological and spiritual lenses, engaging and working with the witness is a way to be fully present and see clearly what is happening within and around you. In other words, to witness what is. You can think of the witness as your guardian angel. However, in this picture, your angel is not an external being with wings and a halo but rather an intangible, inseparable, indispensable part of your being with a 360-degree view of your life and how you live it.

Waking and working with the witness becomes especially important to anyone who has ever dealt with difficulty, and who hasn't? Regardless of who you are, where you live, or your current state of being, your ability to be aware of and witness what is happening at the moment enables you to respond appropriately in a wise and balanced way. This is true whether you are dealing with issues in your body, your breath/energy, or your mind. Here are two examples.

A. and I have been acquaintances for years because we travel in the same creative arts circles in our city. Last year, we met up again in a writing group and got to know each other on a deeper level. At a recent workshop, I shared a blog post I'd written about the witness and asked the group for feedback. A. asked a question about the difference between the mind and the witness.

As an introvert, I need time to think about what I'm going to say. That's hard to do in a group discussion that feels like it's moving at the speed of light while I'm trying to honor the speed limits in my head. I was not happy with the answer I gave him. It felt unfinished and left me feeling unsettled.

After witnessing my discomfort overnight and taking some time to think about the best way to answer his question, I texted him later that morning. It felt like the only way to resolve my discomfort and give him a clearer answer.

Our text exchange follows:

> **Me:** I've been thinking about your question from yesterday about the mind coming up with a way to do something better and I don't think I explained myself clearly. Yes, the mind is conscious of choosing to do something better, but the question is where did that nudge come from? The mind and the witness are interrelated and inseparable, and they work together. So the answer to your question is, it is both mind and witness. Hope that's clearer. ☺

A.: Thank you, Beth—you helped both times. I know that as I mature, I have these "aha" moments, where I realize, "I could do this better by just—"

> **Me:** 👍 Good questions make me a better writer of the stuff I am trying to write. So thank you. ☺

A.: I have been self-inflicting guilt or limitations on myself—and I can just let that go.

> **Me:** Absolutely. And the results last longer if you can figure out why you were self-inflicting guilt in the first place. ☺

A.: LOL—sometimes I know why I have been caught in a pattern, sometimes I realize I do have to ask myself—now why do I do that and where did that come from?

> **Me:** There you go! You done found yo' witness! 😎

A.: Being honest and approachable to oneself is one of the wonders of the world.

> **Me:** It's the biggest wonder and the most fabulous.

A.: It has given me my "sense of agency."

> **Me:** 👍 It's always better to have your own rather than letting somebody else be your agent because they are always going to take a large percentage of your results. LOL.

A.: WOW—Never put it all together like that—but you ain't neva' lie!

> **Me:** Then, grasshopper, I have succeeded in my mission. ☐

When we finished, I felt lighter. I had witnessed and addressed my discomfort and, as a result, confirmed my friend's understanding of his self-awareness and his journey to find clarity. And yes, it looks like I'm kind of addicted to using emojis and may need to do some witnessing on that.

In the chapter, "The Sky Is Blue, But Why Are You?" I wrote about witnessing my periodic "blue funk days" while in the middle of experiencing them and how I discovered something interesting every time. I stew, grouse, bitch and moan, but when I engage the witness, I often find myself chuckling or having intuitive flashes that become ideas for writing, home decoration projects, or *aha* moments that lead to understanding why I'm in a blue funk in the first place. Now I am more aware of the blues when they first pop up. I have learned to ride the emotional wave to see if it has anything to teach me. I no longer try to cut it short and miss out on any new self-awareness tidbits that might be lurking in its recesses.

Mindful awareness is another way of understanding what it means to work with the witness. It is easier said than done, which is why it requires discipline and practice. When I seriously began to work with my witness, it was initially hit or miss, and often came as a delayed reaction.

I first experienced this during my second marriage. We were going through some major rough patches, and I was pretty miserable. I was preparing to attend a training retreat for yoga teachers. My husband was not happy about it and had done everything he could to persuade me not to go. He laid the guilt on heavy and spread it thick on all sides. He told me I was selfish. He threw every trick in the emotional manipulator's handbook at me short of lying on the floor and throwing a tantrum. I professed my love, tried to explain how important this trip was to me, and kept as calm as I could to avoid escalating the drama. It didn't work. So leaving the drama behind, I packed my bag and left.

Midway through the weeklong training, I woke up around three in the morning. Something visceral and weird was going on with my body. Waves of something were rolling from my hips to my head. It felt like I was lying in shallow water at the beach with warm ocean waves rolling over my body. I panicked. I thought I was having some kind of seizure. Then something told me to just lie still and watch. (The witness?) So I did.

I felt the waves roll up one after another, and I was finally able to recognize the waves as emotion. Emotion? Yup, emotion. They were waves of anger and sadness coming from calm, no-drama, rational, reasonable me. I was amazed. When it was over, I was puzzled but was able to go back to sleep. The next day around lunchtime, I had a delayed *aha* moment. I realized the emotions were connected to the day I left home to come to the training. I had done my typical no-drama response to try to keep the peace and did not recognize how I really felt until my body "talked" to me during that early morning experience. I had to wait until my mind could translate the body talk, which took several hours. The witness woke, but it was a delayed reaction.

That was years ago, but that experience encouraged me to work my witness as often as I can. I may present my calm, no-drama, rational, reasonable self to the public, but I no longer stuff my emotions. I can experience and manage them in real-time so my body doesn't have to talk to me later through indigestion, headaches and mysterious middle of the night episodes.

The witness brings awareness to what you think, feel, believe and do, and the habits and patterns that inform why you think, feel, believe and do what you do. The witness is the agent of awareness, acceptance, integration and change. Your mind uses language, but your body speaks with feeling and sensation. If you know how to listen and interpret the messages that come from every aspect of your body, breath/energy and mind, you will do a better job of managing your life. Recognizing and engaging the witness is an important way to create conscious awareness.

Waking the witness and using it to help you navigate life becomes especially important when you are facing tough times, such as dealing with a chronic or terminal illness, facing the loss of an important relationship, or dealing with a crisis. Your ability to witness enables you to respond in a wiser and more balanced manner.

Here are two conscious relaxation practices for waking the witness.

Practice: Awareness of Sensations
Quality to Embody: Observation

SENSATION CAN BE DEFINED AS AN impression, perception or feeling in the body, breath or energy, such as tingling, pulsing, heaviness, firmness, tightness or ease. It can also feel like stretching, pain, discomfort, a change of temperature, or connection with a surface. Emotions also express themselves through sensations, such as feeling hot under the collar, heavy with grief, frozen with fear, or buoyed by happiness. Because these sensations are tangible and accessible through your five senses, awareness of sensation is an effective starting point to enhance your ability to witness.

Note: It will be helpful to record the practices on your phone, computer or tablet. Some people like a slow deliberate pace and others may wish to move through the steps quickly. Depending on your pace, this exercise may take five to ten minutes, or longer.

INSTRUCTIONS

1. Take a position you can comfortably hold for the length of the practice. You can lie down as long as you remain awake and alert.

2. Close your eyes. If you choose to keep them open, soften your gaze or look down toward the floor if you are seated.

3. As you move awareness slowly through your body, breath, energy and mind, observe, sense and feel any sensations that are present.

4. If you catch yourself judging what you find, observe that.

The full practice encourages you to witness your body, breath, energy level, mind and emotions. However, feel free to select and focus on one or more parts that feel most comfortable and natural for you.

One of the best times to practice is in the morning upon waking (hopefully naturally, not because the alarm went off). When you wake up naturally, there is the possibility of experiencing a few delicious "me time" moments before you roll out of bed, head to the bathroom, and start planning the day. It's a perfect time to practice conscious relaxation. It's also helpful to practice before bedtime if you have trouble falling asleep.

As you move through the practice, become aware of and label, in one or two words, everything you notice, sense or feel at its most basic. Let your attention follow the instructions as closely as you can.

Physical

If you feel any part of your body in contact with the bed, label it with the sensations you experience.

> soft
> hard
> scratchy
> smooth
> rough
> other?

If you feel sensation in your body, label it in terms of what it feels like.

> itchy
> painful
> stiff
> tingly
> open
> other?

Energetic

Breath

If you become aware of your breathing, label it with the sensations you experience and where you feel it.

> chest rising
> belly falling
> inhaling
> exhaling
> breathing deeply
>   (or shallowly)
> other?

Energy

If you become aware of your energy level, label what it feels like.

> tired
> balanced
> awake
> calm
> steady
> other?

Mental

Thoughts	Emotions
If or when you become aware of thoughts, label them in terms of their characteristics.	If or when you become aware of emotions, label what they are.

Thoughts

helpful (or not helpful)
judging
planning
remembering
analyzing
other?

Emotions

angry
sad
fearful
anxious
excited
other?

When you finish the exercise, begin to stretch, move and prepare for the day. If you have time, journal or draw any impressions or sensations that stood out for you.

The Shelf Meditation

The first time my yoga teacher read this to the class, we were outside in the Florida sunshine lying on our mats on the grass, feeling warm and peaceful. This remains one of my favorite meditations.

Here is my version of the Shelf Meditation.

INSTRUCTIONS

Make yourself as comfortable as possible. You can lie down, sit up, or settle into any position that will help you relax and feel at ease.

Visualize a shelf. It can be made out of anything you like, wood, glass, stone and so on. As you move through the meditation, place everything that changes in your life on the shelf. At the end, you can take back everything you put on the shelf, but your attitude about some of them may have shifted.

First, place on the shelf an image of your purse or wallet, cell phone and everything symbolically connected with your identity: name, address, driver's license, health insurance, credit cards, phone number, email, contact list, apps, etc. Notice that everything connected to your identity can be put on the shelf, but you are still here, independent of them.

(Long pause.)

Now, place on the shelf an image of your friends and family. Remember you are taking a little vacation from them. You will return to them at the end of the exercise. Notice that although they may be dear to you (or not), you are independent of them.

(Long pause.)

Now place on the shelf all of your life experiences up to this point in time: the good, the bad, the beautiful and the ugly. Include the joys and sorrows of your life. They too can be independent objects for you to observe. Notice that the way you perceive these experiences may be very different from the way you perceived them when they happened.

(Long pause.)

Finally, place an image of your body on the shelf and take a look at yourself from outside of your body. Observe everything you see without judgment. Notice that even your body can be an object to observe.

(Long pause.)

Now notice who is observing everything on the shelf. Try to place that observer on the shelf. You will discover that the observer can't be placed in space and time like everything else on the shelf. The observer sticks like glue. No matter how hard you try to put it on the shelf, it remains the center of yourself, nearer to you than your body.

(Long pause.)

Notice now the qualities of the observer, which we call "consciousness." It is not separate from existence. The world around you and the objects on the shelf are all parts of the same consciousness.

(Long pause.)

Take a moment to notice and witness that unlike everything on the shelf, this consciousness is not limited by space. It cannot exist in the body since the body is on the shelf. It is not limited by time because in the few minutes it took to do this exercise, it's possible everything on the shelf may have changed, but this consciousness has not.

Now notice that this consciousness is whole and content. Although it may be a part of life on the shelf, its sense of satisfaction, peace, joy and enlightenment is innate and does not depend on interactions with any of the objects on the shelf. This sense of wholeness is bliss.

Notice and witness this sense of wholeness and allow it to expand through your entire being in a way that feels comfortable. Know that this wholeness, this consciousness, this freedom from limitation, is your true nature. Rest in this wholeness for as long as you like.

(Long pause.)

When you feel a sense of completion, begin to slowly move your fingers and toes.

Stretch in any comfortable way. As you begin to return to full awareness, take a moment to reflect on your relationship with everything on the shelf. Has anything changed? Do you see anything differently? Where should you place your priorities? What changes, if any, would you like to make to align your life with this sense of wholeness? Reflect, contemplate, journal or draw about this if you wish.

Re-establish your relationship with everything you put on the shelf—your identity, friends, family and your life experiences—but now do it using any new perceptions you may have gained by waking your witness.

Remember, your witness is as close to you as your body, breath and mind. All you need to do is notice it, wake it, listen to it, and work with it.

IT'S COMPLICATED:
MOVING TOWARD EQUANIMITY

*Happiness is when what you think, what you
say, and what you do are in harmony.*

— Mahatma Gandhi

"It's complicated." That was our tour guide speaking from the
front of the bus as it rumbled toward La Habana (Havana).
She was describing the history, politics and economics of Cuba. On
the first day of my 10-day cultural trip to Cuba with Global Arts/
Media, I learned that, despite certain guarantees from the Cuban
government (free housing, education, healthcare and a monthly
ration of food for each family), life is hard. Living in poverty is a
daily reality for many Cubans, who supplement their meager sala-
ries by selling whatever they can. Many simply beg, and American
tourists are their targets.

When approached by Cubans selling books, CDs, caricature
sketches, or food, or simply asking directly for money, our guide
informed us that the appropriate response for refusal was "No,
gracias." She told us we could expect to repeat that phrase many

times since once would not be enough for those who wanted our dollars or convertible pesos, called "CUCs" (special tourist currency).

How true that turned out to be.

Dealing with the street vendors was easy. Since there was an exchange involved, my answer always came after a few seconds of conscious thought, either "yes" I wanted what they were selling or "no, gracias." Dealing with beggars was different. I'd seen people begging on television travel shows, but I had never experienced it.

Before leaving on this trip, I did what I do every December—I sifted through the pile of solicitation letters from nonprofit organizations and wrote checks to those that feed, clothe and provide medical care for the poor and that help children. But to give money to people who walked up, looked me in the eye, and asked for it with an open, expectant hand? That was unnerving and I said, "no, gracias."

As an introvert, I felt really uncomfortable. This was complicated by residual guilt and the feeling that "maybe I should have."

Then two things happened.

I was standing outside Artesanos Cubanos, an artists' collective, looking at my purchases—a necklace and a beautiful hand-carved box with the yoga om symbol on the lid. I heard two sounds, a tapping and a clinking. When I looked up, I saw him. His blind eyes were filmed over and unblinking. The cane in his left hand tapped the cobblestones. His right hand shook a can with coins in it. He made his way carefully past me and continued down Obispo Street. Immediately and without conscious thought, I wove my way through the throng of tourists and locals to drop a handful of coins into his can. "Gracias," he said.

"Por nada," I replied.

The next day, again spontaneously and without conscious thought, I gave money to a man with one leg who was in a wheelchair.

He silently held out his hat as he sat by the fence at the Plaza de Armas, where our tour bus had dropped us off.

Back home, the phrase "It's complicated" filled much of my mind-space. I realized I needed to call on my witness and do some reflection. After thinking and reflecting for a couple of weeks, I came up with three questions I wanted to answer. This allowed me to put the experience in a context that would give me some measure of peace with my residual guilt and the "maybe I should haves."

1. Why was I so focused on this part of the trip rather than the artists and musicians I met and the culture I experienced?

    I needed to acknowledge my response and take time to understand it.

    The art and cultural experiences were rich, informative and enjoyable. Coming face-to face with begging was not. I wanted to confront the "why" behind my emotional response to the real and personal face-to-face begging.

    And at this stage of life, being free-tired (I prefer "free-tired" to "retired"), I find myself blessed with time and an inclination to think about how best to apply wisdom and balance to the art of enlightened living for the time I have left on the planet. So I dug deeper.

2. What factors, conscious and unconscious, influenced my responses?

    I needed the answers to two questions. What did I know? And what did I observe?

    My observation of the two men I gave money to was a direct experience of their life. One man was clearly blind. If he had worn sunglasses, I might not have known that. The other clearly had only one leg. They did not ask for money, so my discomfort button did not get pushed.

My experiences with face-to-face begging felt more complicated. Although I knew something about poverty in Cuba, I could not learn their personal stories from either observation or inference. And since I don't speak the language, other than a few common words and phrases, like "hello," "goodbye," "good morning," "thank you," and "how much does that cost," direct communication was not possible. And as an introvert, I would not have asked.

3. Did I respond appropriately?

This one got really complicated. It took a lot of reflection and witnessing until I had my answer. Many Eastern philosophies hold the idea that to be enlightened, one needs to be able to look upon joyful, happy, pleasant situations, and tragic situations that cause suffering with a measure of indifference.

The word "indifference" threw me until I got a handle on a deeper meaning. Indifference is often misconstrued as apathy or not caring, so I checked other meanings and settled on equanimity. It felt right. "Equanimity" means mental or emotional stability or composure, especially under difficulty, tension or strain.

My experience with the man who was blind and the man who had one leg was peaceful. My response was immediate. There was no emotional charge, either positive or negative. There was equanimity. Even though I felt compassion toward those who asked for money, I did not feel equanimity, as my discomfort, residual guilt, and the "maybe I should haves" clearly showed. I reacted rather than responded. If I felt equanimity, regardless of what action I took, there would not have been the strong emotional charge.

This was the *aha* witnessing moment that clarified my confusion and discomfort, and raised two more questions. How does one respond to both perceived joy and suffering with equanimity? Is it possible to experience life's ups and downs in this five-sense material world without emotional charges?

The answers, for me and for many of us, are both complicated and simple. In the beginning, it can feel complicated when we grapple with the idea of equanimity. It becomes less complicated as it slowly filters through our thinking and witnessing, and is integrated into our being.

So, it looks like I have my work cut out for me; lots of thinking, mulling, contemplation and practice.

With this new awareness, I can begin to practice having equanimity toward everything. I am sure it will be a lifelong slog. I will take one step forward and two steps back, then repeat it over and over again. The concept of equanimity is now "top of mind" and will be a conscious part of how I live every day.

Conscious relaxation and meditation are the recommended practices for witnessing and dealing with many personal issues. Conscious relaxation is a regular part of my life, but adding meditation proved to be challenging, mostly because I was under the impression you had to be able to stop your thoughts.

Reading books about how to meditate confused the hell out of me. So many experts, so many techniques, so many teachers, and too many choices. Finally, I stumbled across a book by Daniel Goleman called *The Meditative Mind* that cleared up most of my confusion and provided me with some context and clarity. This made me eager to attend a retreat and learn more.

I bit the bullet and signed up for a three-day retreat with Ruth Denison, whom I'd never heard of before. According to her write-up, she was the first Buddhist teacher to lead an all-women's retreat and the first teacher to use movement and dance to teach students how to meditate. I was intrigued by what I read about her teaching style. It seemed accessible to anyone.

On the first day, we were offered the option of sitting in chairs. She stressed that finding comfort in our physical position was important to the process, and she had us do a few movements before we sat. That was the clincher for me as a body-centered, movement-loving person. By the time we sat, my muscles had been stretched and relaxed, my breathing had slowed, and I was then able to sit and do a reasonably decent job of focusing on my breath. (Embracing her philosophy that comfort mattered, I sat in a chair.)

That was then. This is now. Do I meditate twenty minutes every day? For many years, the answer was no, I do not. I went through on-again, off-again periods. I did better if I approached the practice with no attachment to a time, technique, or specific outcome, like reaching a meditative state. I also did better when I was a part of a class or group. The energy of others around me supported my process.

Last year, I found a technique that felt right, and I committed to starting with one minute a day. As I write this, I've worked my way up to twenty-one minutes a day. Over the past year, I've missed no more than four days.

Here's the technique I've been working with. I like the simplicity of it.

Practice: Meditation on the Breath
Quality to Embody: Equanimity

CONCENTRATION MEDITATION MAY BE A GOOD choice for you if you have a very active mind. Having something to focus on acts like an anchor for the mind. Choosing a technique and committing to practice it is the one aspect of meditation we control. And we do it with no expectation of the outcome.

The formal name for this ancient yoga meditation technique is "Ajapa Japa," which means, "constant awareness." This technique has many stages. This is the first stage.

INSTRUCTIONS

1. Sit with your spine comfortably aligned.
2. Relax your chest and shoulders.
3. Close your eyes or keep them slightly open with your gaze toward the floor.
4. Start deep, rhythmic breathing with an awareness of each inhale and exhale.
5. Begin visualizing your incoming breath moving upward from the navel to the throat, and the outgoing breath moving downward from the throat to the navel.
6. When the mind wanders, bring it back to the breath and the visualization.
7. Practice for as long as you are comfortable.

If you decide to try this and find it difficult to sense, feel or visualize the breath, imagine it as an elevator. The following visualization works to introduce meditation to children. So why not for us grown-ups?

1. As you breathe in, imagine that an elevator is rising from your belly to your throat.
2. As you breathe out, imagine the elevator dropping back to your belly.
3. When your mind wanders bring it back to the image of the elevator, rising and falling as you breathe in and out.
4. Practice for as long as you are comfortable.

Any meditation practice, as casual, dedicated or rigorous as it may be, will help you be calmer and more resilient. Over time, the practice can help you witness your reactions and responses to uncomfortable personal situations and increase your understanding of complicated cultural issues, like racism, sexism, war, social injustice, or poverty, and face them with a measure of equanimity.

As individuals and as members of the human race, we all have a very long way to go. After all, it's complicated.

CULTIVATING CONSCIOUS CHOICE

*Yesterday I was clever, so I wanted to change
the world. Today I am wise,
so I'm changing myself.*

— Rumi, 13ᵗʰ-century Persi~~an~~ ~~~~ ~~~~ ~~~~

They say there's nothing new under the sun, so it's no surprise we have a modern-day version of Rumi's wisdom.

*I thought I could change the world. It took me
a hundred years to figure out I can't change the
world. I can only change Bessie. And honey, that
ain't easy either.*

— Dr. Annie Elizabeth "Bessie" Delany,
in 1995 at the age of 103[28]

Dr. Bessie is right as rain! Change "ain't easy." But cultivating your skill and ability to embrace conscious choice will help you

---

28 *Having Our Say: The Delany Sisters' First 100 Years*, by Sarah and A. Elizabeth Delany with Amy Hill Hearth, was first published by Kodansha America in New York in September 1993 and was on the New York Times bestseller lists for 105 weeks.

make and manage the changes you need for clarity, contentment and resilience. So, what is a conscious choice? Why should you think about making more of them, and what are the stumbling blocks?

A conscious choice is a decision you make after considering your options, possible outcomes, short and long-term consequences, and your ability and willingness to accept and work through them. Conscious choices range from everyday life stuff (what to eat, when to wash the dishes, what to wear) to larger life stuff (what car to buy, where to live, what job to take) to the serious life stuff (managing finances, starting a family—or not—dealing with loss and emergencies).

Are there stumbling blocks? Oh hell to the yes!

I use the term "stumbling blocks" though because the word "obstacle" feels like a tall wall of solid concrete with no ladder in sight to help us climb up and over. Stumbling blocks remind me of the wooden alphabet blocks I played with as a child. They may be all over the place, but we can kick them out of the way and clear a path with one foot and a little focus. It's doable.

The four stumbling blocks I want to share with you are:

1. reacting to impulses.
2. sleepwalking through life on autopilot.
3. correctly assessing the situation.
4. overcoming inertia.

Impulses are those knee-jerk reactions that lead to outcomes that are, all too often, not in your best interest or aligned with your goals. If you find yourself regularly reacting impulsively, be aware that this pattern of behavior might eventually complicate your responses to serious life issues. Then you may be faced with a series of difficult decisions, which will affect you and your significant others. There are no guarantees. Stuff happens, but it's wise to minimize the complications when we can.

For example, I have a sweet tooth and sometimes, seemingly out of nowhere, I get an impulse to have something sweet, usually chocolate. (I'm a chocoholic.) There are two ways to think about this.

If I act unconsciously, I move directly from impulse to action. My hand dips into my chocolate drawer and... Booyah! A piece of chocolate is inhaled. (Yes, I have a drawer in my kitchen dedicated to bars of dark chocolate. At least it's the healthy kind.)

However, when I practice the art of cultivating conscious choice, I catch that impulse as it arises, call on the witness to consider the consequences of my anticipated action, and ask myself, *Why am I feeling this? Where did it come from? Do I really need a chocolate hit now? Am I willing to accept the consequences since chocolate indulgences after 3 p.m. mess with my digestion?* Sometimes my answer is yes and sometimes it's no. The skills involved are to stop and observe before making a choice.

... may seem like a small thing that brings momentary pleasure with few, if any, consequences. But looking long-term, if I react unconsciously to every impulse for sweets, given my family history, I could be faced with major consequences down the road, like high blood pressure, heart disease and stroke. Any one of these would require me to make important decisions that would involve my family and affect my healthcare and quality of life in significant ways. Even if genetics weren't a concern, any long-term consequences could be traced to a series of seemingly small, unconscious and impulsive, but delicious, choices.

Another stumbling block is sleepwalking through life on autopilot. How often, and in what situations, do you let yourself be carried along like a tree branch swept downstream in a fast-moving river, driven by currents of deep-seated thought patterns, beliefs and habits?

Many of us encounter this stumbling block as we move through our lives. G.'s experience illustrates this.

> G. worked as director of operations for a company where a small group of full-time employees was charged with performing a wide range of tasks for a sometimes-absent owner. This left G., a self-defined jack-of-all-trades, to take on the role of running the company. Because she did not have a written job description, she felt an obligation and responsibility to do everything and take care of everybody, continually placing the needs of others and the company before her own. This situation dominated the choices she made and, not surprisingly, added to her growing stress levels.
>
> She finally stopped to consider her situation and realized she was acting out of an unconscious tendency to be perfect. She said, "Although these beliefs (I must be perfect, I am responsible, I am loyal, I am selfless) contribute to a high quality of work and compassion for others, which is necessary in my field, it also leads to periods of frustration, depletion and burn-out if not managed. Recently, I have been consciously establishing boundaries—reminding myself that ultimately it is not my company."

Her boundaries consisted of making conscious choices for taking time out for self-care and requesting a written job description so there is "an agreed understanding of my role within the company."

Three months after she told me this, she still had not received it, but because she had gotten clear on the source of her stress and the perfectionism fueling it, she was able to begin making conscious and clear choices to address her work situation. She was better able to communicate her feelings to her co-workers and her sometimes-absent owner when she noticed her frustration building.

The point for you and me, as it was for G., is to ask ourselves: What unconscious core beliefs are behind the choices we make in our work, home or social lives? And at a deeper witnessing level, where do those beliefs come from, and how strongly do they influence our unconscious choices that often leave us sleepwalking through our lives on autopilot?

Like G., I am a recovering perfectionist and have control issues, especially around time. Barring an accident, natural disaster or an act of God, I. Am. Never. Late. To. Anything. That would be unacceptable behavior. And the other side of the coin is also true. I do not like to wait for anything or anyone, especially my family.

And my family is always late. If I tell them dinner will be at two o'clock when I actually mean to serve it at three, they show up at five. For years, my perfectly timed dinners ended up sitting on the stove, languishing on hold, and getting cold. I, on the other hand, would be hot, frustrated, pissed and stressed while my mind took a "what the hell is wrong with them" journey.

The last time this happened, we made arrangements to meet at a local restaurant at 6:30 p.m. I made reservations and, of course, got there on time. When they didn't show up by 6:45, I fussed and fumed, called the waitress, and ordered a drink, an appetizer and my dinner. Through gritted teeth and a churning mind, I ate and resigned myself to wait. At 6:50, I got a text from my sister-in-law saying they were running late and would get there by 7:15. They arrived at 7:45. While they ordered dinner, I silently cursed into my dessert.

My sister-in-law's family is my family too because we all grew up together in a small New England town. One year Thanksgiving was going to be held at her nephew's new home. I asked what time. He told me four o'clock. Perfect, I thought. I told him I would make my Aunt Lucy's corn pudding recipe, jacked up with a little bourbon—my addition.

You know I got there at four o'clock. He met me at the door and said, "Wow, you're early!" I was gobsmacked. (That's an old-fashioned word meaning completely, totally and utterly astonished.)

He invited me in. No one else was there, the table was not set, and he and his girlfriend had just put the turkey in the oven. *Say what?*

Once again family dinner was late. This time by three and a half hours!

Now, I know there's such a thing as "Colored people's time." It's the stereotype that African Americans are incapable of punctuality and are chronically late to events and functions. I don't think it has anything to do with being incapable of punctuality. We're on time to work every day because time is money. I think it's a cultural attitude where being on time for social events is, well, let's say "flexible." Folks show up when the energy "feels" right. The pressure to respect the clock for all events, work or social gatherings seems to be more of a Western European construct. I should understand that as I am clearly a person of color, but somewhere, at some level of my mind, there was a serious unconscious disconnect.

And then it hit me. In the middle of bitchin' about my family (and other folks) being late and keeping me waiting, I suddenly realized I was the one who was late. Oh, not in terms of showing up for family, friends and appointments. No, I was late in showing up for myself, for failing to understand that my issue was not with my family's lateness.

My struggle was between having my expectations met and my incessant need to be on time for two reasons. One, because I did not want to upset anyone even though it was crystal clear the family didn't care one way or the other. And two, as long as I was on time, I could take a self-righteous position and do the "I'm right, they're so wrong, and I'm better than them" perfectionistic dance of delusion. I had been sleepwalking through this issue for years. Clearly, I needed an intervention. So I gave myself one.

With this new self-awareness, I had three options: change the situation, change myself, or leave. For personal "waiting" stuff like lines at the grocery store, bank or doctor's appointments, I could always change or re-schedule, but family gatherings are a bit more complicated. If they're at my house, the food is cooked and folks are on their way—late, but on the way. I can't change and I can't leave because I'm hosting.

My family will never change, so now, instead of unconsciously fuming, I catch myself in the act, put on some music, and dance it out while I wait. This way, by the time folks arrive, I can greet them calmly and point the way to the table, the plates and the microwave.

For gatherings held at their homes, I could will myself to arrive late, but that's not a comfortable option—yet. So my interim plan is to arrive on time because that's how I roll. But when I show up on time (early from their standpoint), I cool my jets by shifting into a gracious mode and offering to help. I know that moving and doing will keep me from letting the situation work my last nerve.

Changing these situations was highly unlikely. Leaving wasn't a good option either. The only choice left was for me to change myself. And as Dr. Bessie said, "Honey, that ain't easy either." True, but the effort brings a measure of peace.

Cultivating conscious choice helps with big and small life decisions. Am I 100 percent there yet? Of course not, but I am on my way, choice by conscious choice. It's a process.

Another stumbling block on your path to cultivating conscious choice is the ability to correctly assess the situation you are confronting.

A couple of factors that can block your correct assessment of an issue or situation are:

- information overload or having too much information.
- not having enough relevant information.
- overconfidence in your knowledge and opinion.
- impulsiveness. (Yep, that stumbling block shows up here as well.)

That certainly was true about my two marriages. My failure to correctly assess those situations put me into the deepest valleys of my years on planet earth. Those choices took me through a divorce, emotional abuse, widowhood and financial disaster. Other than the birth of my son, the consequences of those two choices were difficult and painful. Well... Let me clarify that. Giving birth was difficult and painful, but the result was watching a marvelous human being grow into himself. That was 100 percent worth it!

The other upside was that I now view those marriages as teachers and guides that led me to myself. Because of those experiences, I started a self-awareness journey that continues to help me face, trace, embrace and deal with my issues.

The last stumbling block to consider in this chapter is overcoming inertia. Inertia, simply put, is a tendency to do nothing or to remain unchanged.

This scenario plays out in all sorts of ways, especially when I try to follow national exercise guidelines. Getting my behind to the gym for exercise classes is an example. Sometimes I feel glued to the couch. Maybe the weather doesn't cooperate, or I'm low on energy and motivation. It's a struggle. It requires huge nuggets of self-discipline to get up, pour myself into workout clothes, get myself into the car, and drive to the gym, or to go outside and take a walk.

What helps me make the conscious choice to overcome the impulse and pull of inertia is knowing that, if I don't, the string of don'ts will eventually develop into something unhealthy. My arthritis and osteoporosis will worsen. My generally glass-half-full outlook will shift, and the inability to stick to and keep my health resolutions will slowly falter, dry into dust, and blow away. So as easy as it might be to do nothing, I make the conscious choice to exercise because I *always* feel better and lighter when I do. This works about 80 percent of the time. I am being honest here. It's a process.

Let's face it. We all need help to make our choices conscious. Help comes in the form of self-awareness, research, reading, experience, age, sharing with friends, or getting professional help. With self-discipline we can cultivate conscious choices in the decisions we make for the small, large and serious life stuff.

With self-discipline, we recognize our stumbling blocks and can move them out of our way. To build this skill, we need to:

- watch how we respond to impulses.
- stop sleepwalking through life.
- learn how to quickly and correctly assess the situations we face.
- overcome inertia by responding to our stumbling blocks wisely.

Practice: Stop. Observe. Select.

Quality to Embody: Self-Discipline

ONE WAY TO PRACTICE CULTIVATING CONSCIOUS choices is with S.O.S., the international distress signal, but also an acronym for Stop. Observe. Select.

This requires self-discipline. When you find yourself stumped by a stumbling block, stop and observe yourself before you act. Then select the choice that fits your highest intention or give in to the impulse, inertia or habitual behavior with full awareness of the consequences.

Stop

Tune into the feelings and sensations in your body and breath/ energy, then ask yourself the following types of questions.

- How is this situation, issue or problem manifesting itself in my body?
- Do I feel tightness, tension or pain anywhere?

- Are my fists or jaw clenched?
- Am I frowning?
- Does my back hurt?
- Am I smiling?
- Is my mouth watering (especially around food-related impulses)?
- Is my breathing full and deep?
- Is my breath shallow or stuck in my chest or throat?
- Do I feel energy sensations (tingling, warmth, heaviness, lightness, coolness, etc.)?
- Am I feeling energized, tired or fatigued?
- Am I feeling blocked, stuck or held back?

Observe

Witness the mind and emotions.

- Have I accurately and clearly assessed my situation?
- Have I thought through the consequences?
- How will the consequences affect me?
- How might the consequences affect others?
- Can I handle the consequences?
- Is there a habit or belief that might be influencing my choice?
- What am I feeling? Desire? Anger? Fear? Aversion? Joy? Grief?
- Am I content? Anxious? Restless? Excited?
- Am I feeling caught up in my drama?
- Am I judging myself?
- Do I have enough information?
- Should I take action now or give it more reflection?

Select

Choose skillful action. Allow your choices to form. Consider them all and consciously choose one that fits your highest intention. Alternatively, you can choose to give in to your impulse, inertia or habitual behavior. If you choose to give in, you'll need to be aware of the consequences and your ability and willingness to deal with them.

When you apply these steps to the choices you make, you are gradually changing yourself in ways that help you live with clarity, contentment and resilience. And even when it's hard, cultivating conscious choice is worth doing.

Remember Rumi's words. "Today, I am wise, so I'm changing myself."

WHAT DOES THE SHADOW SAY?

*We all have a dark side. Most of us go
through life avoiding confrontation with that
aspect of ourselves, which I call the shadow
self. There's a reason why. It carries a great
deal of energy.*

— Lorraine Toussaint

In psychological terms, the shadow is considered to be the dark
side of our personality, composed of our demons—those parts
of us we either do not know or recognize, or we reject and refuse to
acknowledge. At the same time, there can be positive aspects of the
shadow that remain hidden until we shine the light of the witness
into the dark corners of the self where the shadow lives.

We are like the moon, waxing and waning with one side facing
toward the world. We present those parts of ourselves we want the
world to see to gain attention, approval and love. Then, there is the
shadow and those parts of ourselves we work hard to hide because
we think they are unacceptable.

Most of us prefer to deny we have a shadow side and demons. We find ways to hide those parts of ourselves in the recesses of our subconscious. Does it work in the long-term? Sadly, no, because the shadow and its demons cannot and will not stay locked up forever. They claw and scream and shout. They leak out, climb up, and invade our mental peace, mess with our health, and wreak havoc with our lives. We may want to curse them six ways to Sunday, but they are in there talking trash, taking names, and they seldom, if ever, take a day off. So that means we have to find a way to listen to what they have to say and be grateful for their presence in our lives as teachers and guides.

I'm not sure where I first got the idea I had a shadow self filled with mini-me demons, but as a child, I called it "my bad self." I made a clear distinction between my good self and my bad self. My good self met the expectations of others to show the world I was well-behaved and a good girl with manners. My bad self, hidden away in a corner of my mind, wanted to act on impulse and did not want to follow adult rules. Many sneaky rebellious impulses lurked inside me, like wanting to stand up in church and yell "bullshit" in the middle of a sermon or steal candy from the neighborhood store. I felt them but did not act on them out of fear of the consequences.

I wrote a poem about it when I was nine and started to become aware.

My Bad Self
When my bad self starts talking
My good self starts walking
'Cause my bad self gets me into trouble
Trouble that is double
So when my good self comes to stay
My bad self goes away

I spent most of my childhood pushing my bad self away and most of my adult life refusing to acknowledge it was even there.

At this stage of life, I recognize and acknowledge my shadow and the little demons within it that say "Go ahead, take the cookie, eat the chocolate, and have more. Add some French fries and ice cream, buy that dress, and have that extra drink." Or when I was in the throes of postpartum depression after the birth of my son, "Take that pair of earrings and don't pay for them." Then later, during my post-divorce rebellion, it was "Take another toke of the pot. Why not have a one-night stand? Let's gossip about that person, skip the gym, take those towels from the hotel on your way out, etc." I heard the voices and, most of the time (but not always), had enough self-discipline to answer back, "I hear you, but that behavior is not in my best interest at this time."

It took a lot of work to get to where I am now. I had to learn a basic truth about how the shadow and its demons work, and how to witness and work with them. When I ignored or pushed them away, I experienced mental and emotional distress that translated into physical discomforts, like digestive problems, skin rashes, headaches and constipation. When I began to let them out of the deep dark corners of my mind and listened to them, I learned a lot about the unhelpful patterns that seemed to be running my life.

What are they? Glad you asked. I have identified and am working with these five.

- Perfectionism
- Impatience
- Irritation
- Co-dependency
- Fear of intimacy

Perfectionism is the top layer. I have come to understand that impatience, irritation and co-dependency are symptoms of perfectionism, so when I catch those demons manifesting, I begin the witnessing process and ask, *Why am I feeling irritated and impatient? Am I trying to control or fix something? Did anyone ask me to do that? Why do I think my way is better? Why do I feel a strong urge to control everything? Why did I do that? Did anybody ask for my advice? Am I judging others? Am I judging myself?*

I've learned it is not my responsibility to take on or fix every person I'm with or every situation I am in. I realized I become self-righteously irritated and impatient when my solutions don't work or are not accepted. I know I get overcome by feelings of failure and feel that somehow it's all my fault for not getting it right when things go wrong. I continue to work on the perfectionism demon because the urge is still there, even if I don't act on it as much anymore. Please note that I used the qualifier "as much" in that last sentence because it's a process!

The fear of intimacy is a demon that developed in my adult life as a reaction to difficult relationships with boyfriends and two husbands. And guess what? Turns out my perfectionism, co-dependency and fear of intimacy are closely related. As a kid, if someone showed an interest in me or what I thought or did, I was thrilled. I was right there to give unconditional, co-dependent, "whatever you need me to be or do" behavior to keep the relationship going.

Self-awareness was not an operational word in my relationships with friends, business partners or husbands. I had quite a bit of disappointment in each area until I faced and dealt with the demons that seemed to be plaguing me. I had to take the time to figure out what I was doing wrong and why I was doing it.

I wish I could say I did that all on my own, but I have to thank a social psychologist. I sought her help during the most difficult days of my second marriage. My husband and I tried marriage counseling, but it failed because, after three weeks of talking about his issues with me, the counselor told my husband that at the next appointment we would discuss my issues with him. He refused to go back. This was the catalyst that sent me to the social psychologist who told me that I was co-dependent and would need to deal with that personal issue before I could solve my marital problems. I told that enlightening up story earlier in the chapter called "Nobody Loves Perfect."

After recognizing and accepting the truth, I faced, traced, embraced and replaced the co-dependency demon with a few responsible boundaries, and the demons eased up on their screaming.

There is progress, but it's slow. Once I became aware of who and what the demons were, and how they showed up in my life despite all my efforts to deny, ignore and repress them, I was able to accept them, grudgingly at first, as part of my internal landscape. Slowly, I developed ways to manage their energy and influence.

I have also come to recognize their positive aspects. When managed and in balance:

- perfectionism helps me stay organized in all areas of my life.
- co-dependency reminds me I have a responsibility to set and maintain healthy boundaries in all of my relationships.
- irritation and impatience with loose ends keep me focused and disciplined to finish what I start.
- fear of intimacy helps me make better choices about relationships.

Regina Barreca, an educator and humorist, offers a perfect example of how to deal with the shadow and its demons. Her story titled, "An Emotional Rescue in the Dark Night of the Soul," appeared in her book, *If You Lean In, Men Will Just Look Down Your Blouse*. It illustrates the principles of awareness, acceptance and integration of all parts of ourselves and especially the shadow and the demons we'd prefer to believe we do not have.

In the story, three demons (fear, anxiety and despair) break into a woman's house and wreak havoc. The woman watches them for a time, then boils water on the stove and sets out four cups on the table. Astonished by her actions, the demons ask her what she's doing. She calmly replies:

> I know all of you by now. You've been here before, and you'll be here again. You might as well make yourselves at home. What kind of tea would you like?

The woman was not shattered into pieces because her demons had come to visit. She did not fight them. She simply became aware of them, recognized them, observed them, accepted them, and began to manage their impact on her life.

If you choose to do this, and I highly recommend you do, it will help ground you in self-compassion and forgiveness. You won't be comfortable with everything you find when you begin poking around in your psyche. This self-examination requires that you examine your lifestyle, thinking, behavior patterns and those aspects of yourself that you dislike, deny, repress and hide. That's the juicy stuff. Yes, it is complicated and can be hard.

In the end, the only way to enlighten up is to honestly and accurately shine the light of the witness onto your shadow and its demons. See them. Name them. Accept them. They are a part of you. Look for any positive aspects and use your newfound self-awareness to manage their energy. And if you need help with the process, please get it!

This mindfulness practice will prepare you to share a cup of tea with your shadow and its demons.

Practice: Cultivate an Attitude of Gratitude
Quality to Embody: Gratitude

THE WORD "GRATITUDE" MEANS TO BE thankful and appreciative of something or someone. An attitude of gratitude helps you to live your life with a greater sense of well-being, despite difficulties and disappointments. Feelings of gratitude change the brain by activating the production of dopamine and serotonin, the feel-good chemicals. And as it turns out, making an effort to find gratitude is just as important as experiencing it.

As you deepen your ability to be grateful for the things that make your life pleasant and joyful, you will deepen your ability to find and be grateful for your shadow and its demons, as well as to understand what they are and what they have to teach you. And you will find yourself accepting a sense of radical interconnectedness.

Here are four ways to help you cultivate gratitude. The first two ask you to recognize and appreciate both small everyday details and larger life issues such as health, family, work and friends. The next two encourage you to foster a relationship between gratitude and contentment and suggest ways of accomplishing the goal.

Finding Your G-Spot
Level One. Daily Life Stuff

Start small. Here are a few things to practice being grateful for. Use them as a starting point to create your own list.

- Your car starts up and purrs the minute you turn the key in the ignition.
- The dog snuggles up beside you on the couch.
- Your tax refund is larger than expected.
- The rain stops the minute you leave the house to walk to the bus stop.

- Your child gets an A on a math test.
- During an early morning walk, someone coming from the opposite direction smiles and says, "Good morning."

Level Two. Big-Ticket Stuff

Here's a list of things to be grateful for, despite the difficulties and disappointments that come with each of them. Use it as a starting point to create your own.

- **Health:** Despite aches, pains, moody blues and chronic stuff.
- **Family:** Whether it's functional or dysfunctional.
- **Home:** Even though something's always wrong, such as plumbing problems, roof leaks, or a broken window.
- **Talent and creativity:** From scrapbooking to sculpture and every art and craft in between, even when you get stuck, blocked or frustrated.
- **Friends:** Even the ones who drive you to distraction.
- **Work:** It pays the bills even if it isn't a good fit at this time.

Level Three. Contentment

Gratitude and contentment are closely related. Gratitude can be seen as a subtler aspect of contentment. You can approach contentment by finding a way to be grateful for what you have, even as you may work to have more of something else, such as free time, money, recognition, healthier relationships, or a better job.

It is the ability to remain centered and peaceful. It means not getting too low when daily glitches and life's messes show up (and they will) and not getting too excited when things go 100 percent the way you hoped (and we always hope they will).

Finding the middle ground is not always easy, but practicing gratitude is a stepping-stone on the path to finding contentment with life as it is. Like everything else, it's a process.

Positive Affirmations

These are simple sentences used to describe an aspiration or intention in a way that affirms it's true or is on its way to becoming true. Repeating affirmations can help encourage a positive outlook on life. This one works to cultivate an attitude of gratitude.

> *Thank you for everything.*
> *I have no complaint whatsoever.*

From what I've been able to find, this affirmation is attributed to Sono, a female Zen master, who lived about 150 years ago. I don't know how accurate that is, but I use the affirmation because it gives me a sense of gratitude and contentment when I say it.

Gratitude Popcorn

This is my favorite gratitude practice. Make an intention to notice things to be grateful for throughout the day, every day. As you move from moment to moment and something pops into your consciousness, say "Thank you" silently or aloud and smile. Here are a few things to consider.

- After days of clouds and rain, the sun comes out and the sky brightens. Be grateful for the sunshine. Smile and whisper, "Thank you."

- During the oppressive heat and humidity of summer, a cool breeze passes by. Be grateful for the breeze. Smile and whisper, "Thank you."

- You notice you are feeling anxious. Stop and consciously take three to six long deep breaths. Watch as your anxiety eases. Be grateful for your breath. Smile and whisper, "Thank you."

- While watching the news, you see a story about someone struggling with a serious health condition. Reflect on your health. Be grateful for the fact you are vertical, ventilating and on this side of the ground. Smile and whisper, "Thank you."

To get your bag of gratitude popcorn, remember to tune in to your surroundings a few times a day. When something you can be grateful for "pops" into your consciousness, remember to smile and whisper, "Thank you."

Inspirational Reading

Change can be a hard and painful process. Reading books and articles that contain positive, helpful ideas can help pave the way to wisdom and clarity. I have five shelves filled with books I find inspiring. Here are three of my current favorites.

- *Big Magic: Creative Living Beyond Fear* by Elizabeth Gilbert
- *Only Don't Know: Selected Teaching Letters of Zen Master Seung Sahn* by Seung Sahn
- *Saving Our Last Nerve: The Black Woman's Path to Mental Health* by Marilyn Martin, MD, MPH

As you begin to think about inviting your demons in for a cup of tea, know that the shadow and its demons are not a new concept. "The Guest House,"[29] a poem by Rumi, shows that the shadow and its demons have been known and wrestled with for centuries, long before the field of modern psychology was developed. It is one of my favorites. Here are the first six lines, just to give you a taste...

> *This being human is a guest house.*
> *Every morning, a new arrival.*
> *A joy, a depression, a meanness,*
> *some momentary awareness comes*
> *as an unexpected visitor.*
> *Welcome and entertain them all!*

---

29   Translations by Coleman Barks with John Moyne. *The Essential Rumi.* Harper Collins, 1995.

Your Fifth Layer of Self-Awareness: Bliss

The Taittiriya Upanishad, says bliss is the recognition that all life is one; changeless, nameless and formless. There are many ways to think about your path to bliss. You've probably heard some version of the Hindu proverb, "There are hundreds of paths up the mountain, all leading to the same place, so it doesn't matter which path you take."

The next sentence is less well-known but just as important. It says, "The only person wasting time is the one who runs around the mountain, telling everyone that his or her path is wrong."

It's good counsel to ignore anyone who tells you your path is wrong, and it's wise to listen carefully to those who offer helpful advice, make suggestions, or serve as trusted guides or role models. Ultimately, however, you will need to choose your own path and travel it in the best way you can.

The image of a mountain is a useful one. Picture all but the top of the mountain crisscrossed with a multitude of paths. Some go in straight and narrow lines from the bottom to just below the top, while others with twists, turns and switchbacks still bring the traveler to the desired destination. Others dead-end at boulders, caves and dangerous drop-offs. A healthy level of self-awareness will help you pick the path that is right for you at this moment, allowing you to change paths when needed and deal wisely with the dead ends.

Whether we choose to take a straight and narrow path or one with twists, turns and switchbacks, we will occasionally veer off and hit a road block. When that happens, we may need to stop, set up camp, and chill out while we recognize, face and reflect on the person, place or situation that tripped us up and led us down the wrong path. Once we've faced and traced the issue, we can embrace what we've found, take skillful action to build resilience, and get back on the right path.

Before trying to explain what the mysterious and ineffable fifth layer of self-awareness is (the bliss layer), or how to find it and how to live life after you've experienced it, it's helpful to grasp the difference between bliss and what lies beyond this layer at the very top of the mountain.

From the philosophical, spiritual and religious perspectives, what exists beyond bliss is The Great Mystery, a unified whole, boundless, perfect and complete. Words cannot do justice to name and describe what it is, but they are the only tools we have for writing or talking about it. This is because no one knows for sure what it is, and it's difficult, if not impossible, to define something that can't be expressed in words. That's why it's called "mysterious" and "ineffable."

However, we do have a variety of belief systems, opinions, theories and concepts put forth by mystics, philosophers, religions, scientists, spiritual seekers and ancient wisdom traditions. The Great Mystery has been described as Unity Consciousness, The Divine, Source, The One, God, Cosmic Soul, Unified Whole, Life Force, The Dao, The Field, and Love.

Here are some attempts at defining The Great Mystery.

- The source of all reality that transcends characterization.
- An indescribable "One" that is behind all existing things and is the guiding principle of reality.
- All That Is.

We can visualize and conceptualize The Great Mystery as the top of the mountain. It lies beyond our five layers of self-awareness. We can think of bliss as a pointer, a hint or a trail blaze pointing us toward the top of the mountain. We can work with the bliss layer of self-awareness from the philosophical, spiritual and practical perspectives. These perspectives are not mutually exclusive, because all three play out in our lives whether we're unaware of them, consciously choose to focus on one, or decide to incorporate elements of all three.

The focus of this book is on the practical, so the exploration of our fifth layer will focus on and suggest answers to questions about the meaning and experience of bliss in our everyday lives, such as:

- What is it?
- Where is it?
- How do we experience it?
- What do we do after we experience it?

What Is Bliss?

WHEN WE HAVE A BLISS EXPERIENCE, time loses its linear flow, and space expands to encompass everything as our sense of self as physical and solid seems to disappear.

Some ways to experience this state might be:

- A dimension when concepts of "I" and "you" no longer exist.

- Transcendence of the ego-consciousness into ecstatic unity beyond language, time and space.
- An experience of unutterable joy and peace.

Knowing what brings us joy, along with savoring moments in our lives that "take our breath away," are starting points that over time can take us to deeper experiences of bliss. One way to view these bliss moments, fleeting though they often are, is to think about moments when we feel transported out of ourselves. In this state, our rational thinking mind, ego, personality and sense of self come to a standstill, and we experience a sense of merging with whatever is taking our breath away.

We don't stay in the bliss state. We take mini-vacations there. However, getting there even for a few brief moments is enough to let us know "there" exists. And while we may accept and believe this intellectually, it is only when we get an up-close and personal glimpse of bliss that we know it as true.

Sometimes, we can encourage the bliss state through our decisions, efforts and choices. At other times "shift happens" and bliss appears unexpectedly out of nowhere. In either case, it is important to understand we cannot control its appearance or the experience of it. It's enough to know it exists and to appreciate it after it occurs since we will not know we are in it while we are in it. When it ends, we may find ourselves saying, "Wow! That was amazing!" These bliss experiences are unforgettable and stay with us for our entire lives.

Where Is Bliss?

THAT'S A BIT EASIER TO ANSWER. Bliss is everywhere. It's in us, around us, in front of us, behind us, above us, below us, to the left of us, to the right of us, and it interpenetrates every aspect of our being. It is everywhere and everywhen, waiting for us to open to and receive it.

Here is a story, called "Birds of a Feather," that illustrates this. I've contemporized it a bit, but the essence is true to the original.[30]

> Two birds of golden plumage sat on the same tree. The one above, serene, majestic and absorbed in bliss; the one below, restless and eating the fruits of the tree, now sweet, now bitter. After eating an exceptionally bitter fruit, this bird looked up at the majestic blissful bird and went back to eating the sweet and bitter fruits.
>
> Again, the restless bird looked at the upper bird, hopped up on a higher branch, and continued to eat the fruits of the tree. This eating and hopping upward happened many times until the lower bird reached the upper bird, lost itself in bliss, and realized all at once that the two had never been separate at all.

The lower bird had enlightened up.

How Do We Experience Bliss?

BLISS STATES WAIT PATIENTLY FOR US when our feelings of being separate, imbalanced, confused and distracted have been calmed, stilled and transformed. If we pay attention, we may find ourselves experiencing bliss as contentment and joy when we spend time in nature, establish positive relationships with family and friends, pursue a hobby, volunteer to help others, or enjoy art, music, writing or other creative activity as the artist or audience.

Bliss is also related to the search for meaning: how we choose our values, how we find meaningful work, how we spend our time, and what helps us feel grateful, comfortable in our skin, and enables us to express our full authentic selves.

---

30 Swami Vivekananda. *Meditation and Its Methods.* Vedanta Press & Bookshop, 1976.

It's what Friedrich Nietzsche was referring to when he wrote:

He who has a why to live for can bear almost
any how.

Finding that "why" often results in fleeting moments of bliss that reveal us to ourselves. This is reflected in a line from one of Rumi's poems.

What you seek is seeking you.

Perhaps we've been living our lives according to someone else's rulebook of do's and don'ts, shoulds and musts while ignoring our sense of what would be in our best interest. Or perhaps we've been living life on autopilot with no clue about what would bring bliss, meaning and joy to our lives.

Experiences of bliss that visit us without any effort on our part are wonderful. We can court them in a variety of ways. Here are some examples.

- Step outside our comfort zone.
- Embrace new experiences.
- Pay attention to our dreams.
- Cultivate our natural talents.
- Develop our intuition.
- Bend a few rules and social conventions.
- Keep learning.
- Accept the difficulties life brings.
- Learn the lessons difficulties can teach us.
- Practice meditation.

The five-layers model is a map that can help us find our "why" as we examine every one of our layers of self-awareness. This involves sorting, testing, observing, experimenting, dissecting and classifying until we gain a blissful glimpse of an answer to these two questions: "Who am I?" and "What brings me meaning and joy?"

What Do We Do After We Experience Bliss?

B.K.S. IYENGAR SAYS THIS about living an enlightened up life:

> *For the average practitioner, remember that*
> *learning to live in freedom is a progressive*
> *process, as we free ourselves from the habits of*
> *body, emotions and mind. As we gain greater*
> *skill, we must always be mindful of how to use*
> *our growing power ethically.*[31]

A Zen proverb states:

> *Before enlightenment, chop wood, carry water.*
> *After enlightenment, chop wood, carry water.*

These nuggets of sage advice are meant to keep us grounded in our lives but lifted by the experience of bliss on any level we choose to seek or that chooses to seek us. What changes is our attitude toward life, how we live it, how we manage ourselves, and how we treat others. Whatever your life's work might be, bring all of yourself to it, for when you are fully present, wood is chopped, water is carried, and life happens.

To deepen our understanding of bliss and begin the journey to find and experience it in our lives, we turn to the seventh, eighth and nineth steps of the Nine Steps to Self-Awareness.

---

31 B.K.S. Iyengar. *Light on Life: The Yoga Journey to Wholeness, Inner Peace, and Ultimate Freedom*. Rodale Books. Kindle edition.

Step 7. Find Your Bliss

Questions to consider:

- Have you ever had moments of true contentment and joy in your life?
- What were you doing when you experienced those feelings?
- What would you need to do to bring those feelings to your life on a more frequent basis?

Step 8. Connect to Your Bliss

Suggestions to consider:

- Focus on the journey, your evolution, personal growth and search for meaning.
- Take what you know and seek your bliss, but don't obsess about it.
- Explore, identify and soften any attachments or desire to be in control of the experience.

Step 9. Bring Bliss into Your Daily Life

Work to do:

- Find meaning in your life.
- Define your values.
- Live your values through your actions.
- Share your values with others, perhaps through community service or volunteering.

How can you explore this layer for yourself? The following chapters share information and stories about feeling "good enough," aging gracefully, the importance of treasured objects, and how to find bliss experiences in everyday life. Following each chapter are tips and techniques for practicing compassion, wisdom, exploration and joy.

ENOUGH

I need to see my own beauty and to continue
to be reminded that I am enough, that I am
worthy of love without effort, that I am beau-
tiful, that the texture of my hair and that
the shape of my curves, the size of my lips, the
color of my skin, and the feelings that I have
are all worthy and okay.

— Tracee Ellis Ross

What does it mean to have enough, do enough, and be enough? Maslow's hierarchy of needs is a psychological theory that describes the five basic human needs in the following order.

1. Physiological (air, water and food)
2. Safety (clothing and shelter)
3. Belonging and love (social connection)
4. Esteem (feeling of accomplishment)
5. Self-actualization (achieving one's full potential)

It is difficult to imagine being concerned with doing enough or being enough until your basic needs of having air, water, food, clothing and shelter have been met. So let's start there.

How much of those things are enough? That will vary from person to person and depend on several factors. For me, fortunately, having enough has not been an issue. I was raised in a middle-class family in a small New England town. In any other place, we might have been considered working class because my dad was a janitor and my mom was a secretary. But because of the work ethic of my mom's family in earlier generations, we owned property—two houses on two lots. Both mortgages had been paid off long ago. Our house was next door to my great aunt's house. My brother and I always had somewhere to go after school because my mom worked full-time. My dad worked the night shift, so he needed to sleep during the day. Aunt Lucy's house was a warm and welcome refuge.

Sometimes you know something in your bones. That's how I felt about having enough. I've never worried about having the newest, shiniest, latest anything. Voluntary simplicity is my lifestyle. I keep my cars until they are about to fall apart. I reduce, re-use and recycle clothing, furniture and home decorations. Living in a renovated factory, as I do now, is my idea of a dream home. It's a recycled building after all! I have always had a savings account and continue to save regularly—a lesson learned from my mom and my Aunt Lucy. I have worked since I was sixteen years old. Now that I'm free-tired, I work part-time because I want to, not because I need to. I have enough material things.

It is the intangibles, the next steps in Maslow's hierarchy (social connection, esteem and self-actualization), that were, and sometimes still are, a struggle.

What does it mean to do enough? My issue with this was personal and cultural for many years. In 1980, I was thirty-seven years old, divorced, a single parent with a full-time job in broadcasting and twenty-one credits toward a master's degree in communications. Picture that and read the subtitle. "Middle-class, African American woman/feminist, who tries to do it all and be a credit to the race to prove herself competent, capable, connected and enough."

For those who may not understand the "credit to the race" reference, it is a term used by minority groups whose difference in race or ethnicity implies that each of us needs to earn respect, not only as an individual with distinct talents and skills, but also on behalf of the entire group. The idea here is to help dispel, or at least not add to, negative stereotypes often held by many in the majority. That is a heavy burden, and it weighed on me.

When I was a little girl, many years ago, I was a Negro. By the time I hit college in 1961, I was Black. For the past several decades I have been either Black or African American depending on the company. Anyway, if you are Negro, African American or Black and you see a story about a murder or robbery on the evening news, a part of you always thinks, *Please don't let the perp be Black!* as if one person ever could reflect an entire race. They can't, but the mindset is that if one of us does something wrong or looks wrong, then it affects the whole group. Think about how often young Black men are portrayed as thugs and mistreated by the legal system.

The same holds true about being female. If a male politician involved in an affair or a scandal apologizes and does the public repentance dance with his wife by his side, he is ultimately forgiven and often takes up his place in the body politic again without issue. The same outcome for a female politician in a similar situation does not apply. We continue to live with a double standard for women and being a woman of color means double that double standard.

The cues I was getting from society and my family fed the directive to do it all and be a credit to the race, but inside, I felt crazy. Beneath my struggling and juggling, I was constipated and stressed. I developed temporomandibular joint dysfunction (TMJ). There was not enough time, not enough energy, and not enough of me to go around and do all that was expected of me and all I expected of myself.

It felt like I was being ripped in half. I was active in Black groups and feminist groups and was asked time and again if I felt more discriminated against as a woman or as a person of color. My response? I'm not Black on Monday, Tuesday and Wednesday and a woman on Thursday through Sunday. I'm a complete package. I refused then, and I refuse now, to split myself into some politically correct answer depending on who is asking. So there I was, working my way through Maslow's third and fourth hierarchy of needs: esteem and self-actualization.

I needed to find an answer to the question, "What does it mean to *be* enough?"

Finally, I figured out that if I could recognize or create an internal sense of contentment, I would be able to manage my existential angst and be enough, at least to myself. Some people find esteem and self-actualization in church, some in the creative process, and others in sports. I started my journey to find contentment in one of my favorite places, a brick-and-mortar bookstore.

I scoured the self-help sections looking for a quick fix, a change in diet, a new exercise program, or a different way of thinking. I read them all and tried most of them. Nothing worked long-term. Then I picked up a book by the late Richard Hittleman and discovered yoga. The physicality of it appealed to me enormously. It felt like dancing. I loved to dance. It relaxed me. I needed to relax. It was a perfect fit. I was hooked. I bought books and tapes and practiced alone, in true introvert fashion, waiting for enlightenment and bliss. It seemed like enough.

A few years later, I had enlightened up a few degrees. I got that I could not do it all without risking my health and sanity. I had given up business suits and heels along with several committee and board positions. And yes, external validation from several people and organizations melted away as a result.

I was still struggling with the strong Black woman, credit to the race, and "I am woman, hear me roar" directives, but I was questioning what it all meant. Did I need to fit society's image of what that was or looked like? Could I be a credit to the race and roar on my own terms, in my own voice, and still be me? I didn't know, but I felt myself inching closer to my truth.

It was at a yoga weekend in New York's Catskill Mountains when the idea of being enough shifted from an intellectual concept to a cellular understanding. I was in the middle of a sweat-popping sun salute, struggling to hold up my body on one foot and one hand in a side arm balance.

"Hang in there," said the teacher, "Breathe. Feel your power. Let me hear some deep sighs."

I sighed and hung in. Next came alternate leg lifts and locust pose. I followed along carefully, feeling how much my spine had loosened because of my home practice. Glued to the ground from chin to pelvis, lying on my stomach, I inhaled both my legs off the ground and felt them float up.

"This is a powerful back strengthener," said the teacher, "so squeeze that butt. A few groans and sighs would feel good about now."

My legs ached with the effort, but I groaned and sighed and squeezed and held just a bit longer than I thought I could before lowering them.

At last, Savasana.[32] Relaxation!

"Let yourself blob out on the ground and feel the energy circulate." Her voice was soft, soothing and musical.

---

32   Savasana, or Corpse Pose, is typically the final pose in a yoga class or private session. It is often practiced in a supine position with props, like blankets or pillows, for comfort. The goal is encourage a deep period of relaxation that allows all five layers to balance and integrate.

"Welcome the benefits of the universe. Feel yourself melt into the ground. Breathe deeply. Inhale through the head. Roll the breath down the body. Exhale it out through the toes. Relax."

Being away from home with family and work responsibilities on hold, I found myself at that moment halfway between sleep and wakefulness, floating somewhere between here and there. Grace, bliss, surrender and contentment. Wonderful! As good as sex and better than chocolate!

It's been a long process. It took thirty-seven years for the threads of striving to meet others' expectations and feeling not good enough to tie themselves into knots big enough to feel. Does it matter that it took another thirty-seven years to untie those knots and let the threads dissolve? Nope. In the end, the only thing that matters is that I've found the discipline to work through the knots moment-by-moment, bit-by-bit, and thread-by-thread.

Today, I am a lot better at managing stress. I haven't been constipated in years. My TMJ bite plate sits unused on the top shelf of the medicine cabinet. My yoga practice is much gentler and more contemplative these days and is as important to me as breathing. I no longer think enlightenment will come suddenly, bliss me out, and whisk away my struggles. I rejoice in the fact that underneath the African, underneath the American, and underneath the woman is a being who can occasionally and surprisingly "be here now." In those moments, I can rest amid the chaos and be present in my life with its problems and joys. I can experience it and me at the same time. I am competent, capable, connected and authentic, a credit to universal consciousness in all its forms. And that is enough.

Practice: Turtling

Quality to Embody: Compassion

IF YOU ARE STRUGGLING WITH THE expectations of others along with your own, you are probably very familiar with stress. One of the first things to do is to quit shoulding on yourself. Show yourself compassion. Be kind. As RuPaul, the famous drag queen, says at the end of his reality TV show, RuPaul's Drag Race:

> *If you can't love yourself, how in the hell are you gonna love somebody else?*

Take the time to learn healthy ways to reduce and manage stress. Turtles pull their head and legs into their shells and retreat whenever they feel threatened, in danger or need protection from predators. Being encased in their shells helps them feel safe. Whenever you feel overwhelmed, stressed out, threatened or vulnerable and want to feel safe, try turtling.

The following practices can reduce the effects of stress and, when done separately or together, have these benefits. They:

- slow the breath.
- conserve energy.
- calm the nervous system, the inner critic, and the mind.
- sharpen self-awareness.
- set the stage for feeling enough.

Turtling Using Your Body:
Child Pose

This calms your nervous system and reduces the effects of anxiety and stress.

INSTRUCTIONS

1. Put a blanket or exercise mat on the floor to cushion your knees.
2. Start on your hands and knees.
3. Sit back on your heels.
4. Drop your forehead to the floor.
5. Stretch your arms straight out in front of you or rest them back by your legs. If your forehead doesn't feel comfortable on the floor, rest it on your folded arms or a pillow.
6. Stay in the position for two minutes, or longer if you are comfortable.

MODIFICATIONS

- Do the pose in bed so you don't have to get up and down from the floor. This is easier on the knees.
- If you need to turtle while at work or take a break from working at the computer, you can do this modification in a

chair (or on the toilet if you need privacy). Place your elbows on your lap and rest your head in your hands. Let your shoulders shrug up to your ears. Close your eyes and take a break.

Turtling Using Your Breath:
Whispering Breath

This exercise calms the nervous system and the mind.

INSTRUCTIONS

1. Sit on the floor or in a chair with a comfortably straight spine.
2. Relax your chest and shoulders.
3. Take in a slow deep breath through your nose.
4. Pucker your lips as though you were going to whistle.
5. Let your breath out slowly through your mouth. Pretend you are trying to cool hot soup on a spoon without spilling any.
6. Practice the Whispering Breath for two to three minutes.

Turtling Using Your Mind:
Turtle in the Shell

This hand gesture deepens a sense of grounding, moves energy out of the head, and promotes a feeling of safety and security. In yoga, it is called "Adhi mudra."

INSTRUCTIONS

1. Sit with your spine comfortably straight. Because you are using your hands, this practice can be done anywhere at any time to calm down.
2. Hold your hands in front of your chest with your palms facing toward you.
3. Move your thumbs (the turtle's head and neck) across the palms of your hands.
4. Close your fingers (the turtle's shell) over your thumbs.

5. Turn your hands over and rest them on your legs.

6. The backs of your hands are now facing up.

You can also use an affirmation, such as "I am calm. I am relaxed. I am peaceful." This can be said either silently or aloud.

It is important to recognize that you are enough. Here is a quote that sums it up nicely. A friend shared it with me, and I'm pleased to share it with you.

You are enough. You are so enough.
It is unbelievable how enough you are.

— Sierra Boggess

THREE SHADES OF GRACE

Aging is not an option, not for anyone.
It is how gracefully we handle the process
and how lucky we are, as the process
handles us.

— Cindy McDonald

"Aging is not for sissies." Another quote I bet you've heard somewhere. It typically means that growing old is difficult. A woman in my book group shared this next one, "Aging is a bitch!" And here's one more, "Aging gracefully is an art." This one may be the hardest to fully embody.

We will all age, but some of us will do so more gracefully than others.

As we age, we change. The mirror does not lie. Wrinkles and gray hair appear, muscles begin to lose mass, and relationships with ourselves, our family, friends and society often change. In some cultures, aging earns us status as wise elders to be revered; in others, we are ignored, put aside, and perceived as having little value.

We may begin thinking about the end of life and seeing death as loss, something to be feared, or as a natural transition to something else. That something else often depends on our culture, country, family, religious or spiritual beliefs. Regardless of who we are or where we live or how old we are in this moment, cultivating the capacity to age gracefully will help us move through the inevitable aging process with clarity, contentment and resilience.

What does aging gracefully really mean? The word *grace* means elegance, a pleasing quality of movement, a sense of what is right and proper, or thoughtfulness toward others. It comes from the Latin "gratia," translated as "favor," "charm" or "thanks," and from Latin "gratus," meaning "pleasing" and "grateful." In Sanskrit, this word is akin to the word "gṛṇāti" meaning "he praises."

To age gracefully, we can embrace aging in three shades (or forms): physical, social and spiritual.

Physical Grace

THIS CAN BE DEFINED AS SELF-POSSESSION that conveys a sense of comfort, joy and well-being. Need an example? Here are two.

Recently, while driving to a friend's house for dinner, I coasted to a stop behind a long line of cars at a traffic light. Irritated and knowing I would probably have to wait for two light changes before I could drive on, my lips tightened and my fingers drummed the wheel. Off to my left, I saw a woman dancing along the sidewalk to music only she could hear through her earbuds. She stepped off the curb and dance-walked across the street, never missing a beat. Her movements brought a smile to my face. I nodded my head to the music I felt but couldn't hear. My energy shifted as I watched her, and the moment was transformed. Watching her reminded me of a similar experience when I was the dancer.

It was a James Taylor concert at Tanglewood in Lenox, Massachusetts. My friends and I had lawn tickets on that sunny afternoon. James was playing and singing, and I stood up to dance. I danced and swayed through the whole concert. I did it because the music moved me, and in that setting, no one thinks it's strange to see a woman dancing alone. As my friends and I were packing up our picnic baskets to leave, a man came up to tell me that watching me dance had made his day. Wow!

Physical grace can have a direct impact on others. If we develop our personal style of physical grace, we can express it in how we move, dress, walk and dance as we age. The benefits are flexibility, elegance, strength, artistry, poise and agility, plus feeling comfort and pleasure being in our own skin.

Social Grace

WE ARE WIRED TO BE SOCIAL. Research tells us that having friends and participating in groups is beneficial to our health and extends life.

Talking is a major aspect of socializing. It's the glue that holds friendships and social groups of all types together. We talk a lot among friends and in groups, but how often do we really listen? And how often are we really listened to? Listening is accurately receiving and interpreting messages, whether it is listening to yourself, to another person, or in a group setting.

Think of the last person who actively listened to you and participated in a reciprocal conversation. How did that make you feel? Subtly pleased, seen and heard, I'll bet. People who actively listen demonstrate social grace—the ability to make others feel seen, heard and connected.

Another way to express social grace, especially as we age, is through creativity and a sense of humor.

Norma, one of my regular yoga students, was a great example. Sadly, she is no longer with us, but while she was alive, she was a marvelous example of social grace. She dealt with several health challenges, was a two-time cancer survivor, and suffered from hearing loss. She used compression socks for her swollen ankles, but she cut out the toes of the socks to show off her pedicure. She liked to make rhyming books for her grandchildren, and she wrote books of self-published poetry.

In one poem, her spirit and sense of humor about aging shines through. It shares her memories of once having "perky boobs," a small waist, and joints that did not ache. It also expressed her gratitude for still being active and alive in her 80s.

That is social grace in action!

Spiritual Grace

SPIRITUAL GRACE IS DIFFERENT THAN PHYSICAL and social grace. We can control how we experience and express our physical and social grace. When we practice prayer, meditation or deep self-awareness, we may experience a sense of grace, but we do not control when it arrives or how long it stays. Spiritual grace can be bestowed upon us with no effort or practice on our part. It is a gift.

Here is what Sandy Eimers, a yoga therapist and the owner of băl'•ance yoga lounge & băl'•anced *breath* school of yoga, told me about her experience with spiritual grace.

> It's a state of emptiness and unity I have reached enough times to know it truly exists, but it is elusive and does not materialize on command. My experiences have been fleeting moments. One in particular that I remember very clearly was when my three kids were little. The two girls were giggling outside in the snow on a cloudy day in their brightly colored snowsuits, the baby was asleep for a nap, and I was sitting next to

the patio door with a hot cup of chocolate. There was a very brief moment where I sensed that everything in the world was in the divine right order, and it was an amazing feeling that ended seconds later when the oldest poked the middle child with an icicle and it was over. But I never forgot that moment. Everything was very clear, and it was as if the world stopped revolving for a millisecond and I was filled with bliss and peace.

It is lovely when spiritual grace happens without effort, but practice tills the ground and plants the seeds to prepare us to receive and recognize it when it occurs.

Here is Maria's story. It illustrates how a spiritual practice can transform a difficult situation into a recipe for aging gracefully despite health challenges.

Maria began her professional work life as a holistic orthopedic nurse and is now a functional movement therapist. She learned a lot about how to age healthfully and gracefully from a sudden and devastating accident.

Twenty years ago, as she was riding her bike in Mexico, she was hit from behind by a pickup truck. She sustained a massive brain injury and a broken back. She was told she would probably never walk again unless she had surgery, and even with surgery, there were no guarantees. She refused because, as an orthopedic nurse, she had witnessed many surgeries and observed that many patients who had fusions and rods implanted did not always get better. They often developed more issues. And so, she decided to heal herself holistically. Her orthopedic surgeon was not happy and told her that she should have her nursing license taken away. She made a deal with him; she would come back and have surgery if her healing regimen did not work. In exchange, he agreed to take one of her yoga classes if she was successful.

Fortunately, her self-healing regimen worked. She used time, healthy living, an attitude of gratitude, meditation, yoga practice, and support from friends and family to begin a long, slow process of healing and self-discovery. Now in her sixties, she is walking, running, dancing, teaching yoga classes, managing a yoga therapy practice, and offering workshops and training. She can deadlift 120 lbs. in perfect form. She is an example of how to age gracefully and function optimally.

About aging, she says, "Most of our perspective on aging is in our minds. We do have a biological clock, but I don't believe that aging equates with the body failing." She is still waiting for her orthopedic surgeon to attend one of her yoga classes.

Grace in all of its forms can help us transform the feeling that "Aging is a bitch" or "Aging is not for sissies" into "Aging gracefully is an art," as we take steps to age gracefully and enlighten up in the process.

Practice: Personify Your Three Shades of Grace

Quality to Embody: Wisdom

WISDOM IS THE QUALITY OF HAVING experience, knowledge and good judgment. If you want to age gracefully, developing a measure of wisdom about how you think, feel and act as you move through the aging process will help you to understand aging in general, and your process in particular. Here are a few suggestions for personifying your three shades of grace.

Physical Grace – Move It Until You Lose It

We are all going to lose it at some point, and by "it" I mean our physical agility. That's life. Until that time arrives, you greatly increase your chances of enjoying life if you keep your body as healthy as possible. One of the easiest ways to do that is to move as much as you can in any way you are able to given your level of ability.

Think you may be too old to start? Let the example of these four women help you get going. The late Harriette Thompson became the oldest woman to complete a half-marathon in 2017 at the age of 94. The late Gladys Burrill set a Guinness World Record when she ran a marathon in 2010 at the age of 92.

And then there is Ida Keeling who started running at the age of 67. In 2016 at the age of 101, she ran the 100-meter dash at the Penn Relays in 1 minute and 17.33 seconds to set the world record for women age 100 and over. When she was done, she dropped to the track to do pushups. The crowd roared! At this writing, she is now 105.

Ida's record was then broken in 2017 by Julia "Hurricane" Hawkins, who, at 101, set a 100-meter dash time of 40.12 seconds at the USA Track and Field Outdoors Masters Championships.

You may not be ready to tackle that level of athleticism, but here is an easy morning (or anytime) stretch routine to try out. It can be done seated or standing.

Forward-Backward Bend

1. Stand with your knees slightly bent. If seated, place both feet on the floor with your knees open, feet apart, and spine comfortably straight.
2. Place your hands on your hips.
3. Exhale and bend forward from your hips until your spine is parallel to the floor.

4. Inhale as you come up and gently arch back as far as you comfortably can.

5. Repeat at a comfortable pace six to twelve times.

Side Bend

1. Stand with your knees slightly bent. If seated, place both feet on the floor with your spine comfortably straight.

2. Place your hands on your hips and inhale.

3. Exhale as you bend to the left.

4. Inhale as you return to center.

5. Exhale and bend to the right.

6. Inhale as you return to center.

7. Repeat at a comfortable pace six to twelve times.

Twists

1. Stand with your knees slightly bent. If seated, place both feet on the floor with your spine comfortably straight.

2. Raise your arms out to the sides at shoulder height.

3. Inhale as you twist to the left. Allow your right heel to come up off the floor if that feels natural.

4. Exhale as you twist to the right. Allow your left heel to come up off the floor if that feels natural.

5. Allow your arms to freely move as if they are empty coat sleeves.

6. Repeat at a comfortable pace six to twelve times.

Social Grace – Pay It Forward

Think about the best advice you have ever been given. Why was it so helpful? Make a point to pay it forward by sharing that advice freely with others when the situation feels appropriate.

Avoid giving unsolicited advice though since that is the opposite of a wisdom practice. Instead, practice active nonjudgmental listening. Here are a few guidelines.

1. **Pay attention.** Give the speaker your undivided attention and acknowledge the message. Recognize that what is not said also speaks loudly. "Listening" to the speaker's body language is equally important.

2. **Show that you are listening.** Use your body language and gestures to convey your attention. Nod occasionally and smile to encourage the speaker to continue.

3. **Provide feedback.** Our filters, assumptions, judgments and beliefs can distort what we hear. As listeners, our role is to understand what is being said, reflect on it, and ask questions for clarification.

4. **Try not to interrupt.** Don't try to change the subject or bring the conversation back to you. That frustrates the speaker and limits a full understanding of the message. However, there are times when you may need to interrupt to keep healthy boundaries.

5. **Respond appropriately.** Active nonjudgmental listening is a model for respect and understanding.

   - Be candid, open, honest and compassionate in your responses.
   - Assert your opinions respectfully.
   - Treat the other person as they, and you, would want to be treated.

6. **Listen actively** but set wise healthy boundaries.

Spiritual Grace – Connect

1. **Connect with your attitude toward aging and transform it if necessary.**

   Researchers have found that if we hold a negative attitude toward aging, our health can suffer, but if our mental attitude is positive and we view aging as a time for continued growth and learning, our bodies listen and respond.

2. **Connect with a dream deferred.**

   Many times our dreams and passions arise in childhood, only to be put on the back burner when adult responsibilities take over. What was it you dreamed about doing when you were young? Art? Crafts? Sports? Science? Travel? Cooking? Writing? Think long and hard. Write it down.

   This is an important step in connecting with a dream deferred. You may find a buried treasure waiting inside you to enrich your aging process in some way.

   Elizabeth Gilbert author of *Eat, Pray, Love* has written a book titled *Big Magic* about creative living beyond fear. In it, she makes this point:

   > *The universe buries strange jewels deep within us all, and then stands back to see if we can find them.*

   When you find your jewels, write them down. Then narrow and prioritize the list to the top three or four things you'd like to spend time on. Pick one item, then make an intention to act on it, bring it into your life, and find ways to share it with others.

   Whatever it is, permit yourself to pursue it with wisdom and persistence.

3. **Connect with inspirational ideas.**

What is inspirational for you will be different for your friends, family and others. If you are beginning your search, look around you. Inspirational ideas and sources for finding them are everywhere. You can see them in nature, read about them in books, and experience them through art. You can hear them in music, stories and personal conversations, and feel them in your body and mind when you dance, engage in a favorite hobby, meditate, pray or write.

There are many ways to personify these three shades of grace: physical, social and spiritual. You owe it to yourself to embrace yours.

TRY ON AN ICON

Iconography, good iconography, strives to
convey invisible reality in a visible form.

— Peter Pearson

There may have been a cross on the altar of the congregational church I attended as a child but, if so, I don't remember it. Iconography was scarce in my church. It was very apparent, however, on many lawns in my small hometown. Statues of Jesus and the Virgin Mary were the only ones I saw, so I didn't realize that iconography was part of many religious and spiritual paths.

Understanding the global role of religion and spirituality has always been an interest of mine. I understood Catholics had many saints, and Hindus, an amazing pantheon of gods and goddesses. This is also true of the voodoo religions of Africa and Haiti, and Santeria in Cuba. In Asia, impressive statues of the Buddha dot the landscape along with Kuan Yin, considered to be the Madonna of Mahayana Buddhism. Yoga's icon, the symbol of om, is said to represent the foundational sound and vibration of the universe.

Iconography ranges in form from statues and symbols to pictures and paintings, which hold an established place in the human condition and psyche.

I took a long journey to understand why iconography has such a strong pull for humans. It began with distaste based on ignorance. I have no problem admitting that. Remember, I'm trying to be as honest as I can with all of this.

Watching people prostrate themselves in front of, and pray to, statues made me uneasy and uncomfortable until I learned the difference between idolatry and iconography. Once I understood that people were not worshiping the physical icons themselves but rather were praying to what they represented, I got it. Now I can participate, but on my own terms.

As a writer, I am comfortable with ideas, which are a form of mental energy that can be translated into matter by putting pen to paper or typing words on a computer. After dipping a toe into the shallow end of the ocean of theoretical physics (I would have become a physicist if it weren't for the math), I came to understand that everything I see is energy that has vibrated into a solid state of matter. I know that may sound weird, but read a few theoretical physics for beginners books, and you'll see what I mean. Anyway, when I accepted that, I realized that iconography was another way to represent energy as it moves from thoughts and ideas into physical form. It can connect us to bliss, peace and contentment through the way we express ourselves in our personal environment.

It occurred to me that in the journey to self-awareness, becoming conscious of what we surround ourselves with and how we respond or react to their presence is worth exploring. Understanding who and what the items are; what they represent; when, how and why we acquire or purchase them; where we place them; and why are key questions to ask ourselves.

Once I decided to answer these questions for myself, I took an icon journey of my home to identify the items and energies that spoke to me or represented something I had chosen to incorporate in my life. And since I am a person of action that's what I did. Here are the highlights of my icon tour.

Three Buddhas reside in my condo. I don't have any particular religious faith. I've explored several religions on my spiritual journey and, for a while, I seriously toyed with the idea of becoming a Buddhist. I was and still am attracted to the Buddhist concept of finding the source of suffering and applying the right action to release it. It also happens that the Dalai Lama is very high on the list of people I deeply respect. Because of my slightly rebellious, doubting and skeptical personality when it comes to organized anything with too many rules, regulations, shoulds and should nots, it comes as no surprise that I ran into several speed bumps in my exploration of Buddhist groups.

I was not happy, but also not surprised, to see the lack of diversity in the groups and their leadership. I know this is largely due to cultural and social issues, but at this stage of my life, I choose to put my energy into efforts that are inclusive and diverse. I respect organizations that embrace those concepts, but my experience has been one of being the only grain of pepper in a sea of salt. I am unwilling to spend the last years of my life doing missionary work to increase diversity in social, political, religious or spiritual organizations and groups.

Okay, that's enough of my rant. Here's the 411 (relevant information) on my Buddhas.

Laughing Buddha is the smallest one. He is about four inches tall and made of cheap plastic. He is also the first icon I brought into my space. He was a birthday present from a former boyfriend. I think he did it as some sort of snarky joke. He was pretty sure I'd be pissed because it wasn't chocolate or a piece of jewelry. Does that give you a hint about why he became an ex-boyfriend? Anyway, I loved it. Laughing Buddha has been with me since the early 1980s and has survived five moves with only a broken toe.

Then there is Garden Buddha. He sits on a table in the living room, thirty inches from the ground and facing the entry door. That is feng shui to ensure prosperity finds its way into my home. I think it's working. I consider prosperity to be good health and enough income to cover the bills with a little left over for fun. His eyes are closed in meditation, and his hands rest in a gesture of effortless meditation (a state I'm still attempting to achieve). Photos of my family, many who are here and others who have passed on, surround him. I put a small pink stone heart in his lap to acknowledge that he's sitting in the middle of a huge circle of love and life represented on that altar table.

Lastly, there is the Buddha who wears a hat. He is a Buddha head on a rod anchored in a black marble base. He looks like a Buddha lollipop. He lives in my bedroom on the right side of the headboard and well over the required thirty inches from the ground. He faces the bedroom door per feng shui and Buddha placement protocol.

He wears a hat because I went through a hat craze a few years back and needed a place to put my new collection. One day, I realized the Buddha head would make a great place to hold a few. I chose hats that looked smart and fashionable. Now he sports two snappy, white-brimmed summer hats. I hope this is not considered disrespectful. I think he's slaying the look!

Om is often described as the root sound of the universe, symbolizing all consciousness and the beginning, middle and end of all that is here and beyond our space-time continuum. It is the symbol of yoga.

I think of om as a way to tune or align the body's energy to its healing source in the same way that tuning forks help set musical instruments to the correct pitch. Chanting om feels like that—deep, comforting and aligning. I first heard it chanted in a yoga class. It felt familiar. It felt like a friend. It felt like coming home. I flirted with the idea of getting an om tattoo. I told myself I'd get it when I turned sixty. I didn't. Then I told myself I'd get the tattoo when I free-tired from my full-time job. I didn't. Then I told myself I'd get the tattoo when I turned seventy-one and started to draw down on my retirement investments. I didn't do it then either. I think tattoos are romantic, artistic and rebellious, but I guess I'm not brave enough to decorate my body with one. Instead, I'll be satisfied with the om symbols decorating my home.

My friend Elly gave me my first om. It is screened in black on a yellow throw that covers the futon in my guest room. I think of her every time I look at my futon. It's a way to keep her memory alive. She transitioned off the planet from breast cancer several years ago, and I still miss her.

Om number two came into my life while on a working vacation at the Mount Madonna Center in California. I bought a 10" x 10" engraved gold-plated metal om from the gift shop. I hung it on the wall over a lamp next to my front door. I think of its function as similar to that of the mezuzah Jews place to the right side of their door. It is a reminder of their covenant with God and identifies the home as Jewish. My om reminds me that, according to yoga tradition, I am innately connected to a single source, even when I can't feel it. That source is where I came from and will someday return. I think of Source as the ultimate energy field. Remember, I have a deep abiding "thing" for theoretical physics.

As I shared earlier, I have another om carved into the lid of a handcrafted jewelry box. I bought it at the artist's market on Obisbo Street in Havana, Cuba. Inscribed inside is a Spanish phrase the artist translated for me.

> *I cannot, in a day, change the desert, but I can*
> *make an oasis.*

That's serious bliss food for thought.

My interest in iconography didn't end with om. Ganesha came next. Ganesha is an icon of the Hindu religion. He is represented by an elephant's head on a seated human body. For me, Ganesha's got game, lots and lots of game. "Game" is urban slang for skill, talent and ability, as in, "he's got game."

Ganesha is thought to be the ruler of joy, happiness, success and perseverance in the face of adversity. Who wouldn't want that kind of energy?

Ganesha energy is said to be capable of removing obstacles or putting one in our way to prevent us from making a mistake. This resonated with me and reinforced the importance of reframing difficulties and disappointments and putting them into perspective. It is intriguing to think that a difficulty or disappointment may, in the long run, work out to be a positive thing.

For example, I have always had a desire to live in some type of intentional community. One day in the late 1990s, a friend who knew about my interest urged me to read a story in the local newspaper about a group working to establish a cohousing community. I read the article and learned that cohousing is an intentional community of private homes clustered around a shared community space. Typically, a group of people comes together, pools money, finds land, and builds a community. I immediately joined the group.

One of the potential sites we visited was an old factory across the railroad tracks in a small New England town. I loved the site, the building, the nearby river walk, and the neighboring historical buildings, all within a five-minute walk to the town center. This site did not work out for our group though. The obstacles? The main problem was the difficulty of a group process that required consensus, along with a town government that was not excited about or supportive of cohousing on that site. After a few more years of trying, the group gave up and dissolved.

Major disappointment? Yes, but two blissful blessings emerged from that experience. The core group still meets a few times a month over a potluck dinner. We call ourselves, "Neighbors Without a 'Hood." The name comes courtesy of my good friend who alerted me to the group. And the second is that the town ultimately developed that factory site into fifty condo units, and I'm the proud owner of one of them. It's not cohousing, but with the energy of other neighborly heartbeats and a friendly "Hi. How are you?" around the carports and the mailroom, it's enough. The icing on the cake is that the building is listed on the National Historic Register. My home is an icon!

And in my iconic home sit three Ganeshas. The largest is an elephant-head statue beautifully sculpted in cement, positioned on a metal stand. I saw him in a catalog and ordered him right away. He sits on a small cabinet in the northeast corner of my condo. It turns out this is the best feng shui placement for Ganesha. I didn't know that when I put him there, but I was glad to find the choice I made was the right one. The cabinet sits under a photograph from the mid-1800s of a very distinguished-looking man in a suit and bow tie who is an ancestor on my mother's side. I found the photo in my mom's attic and had it matted and framed. He is part of my family history, and I consider him an icon as well.

The placement of my next Ganesha is not great feng shui, but it works for me. This Ganesha is part of a paper pop-up book, a gift from one of my students. Paper Ganesha rests on top of a small half-moon-shaped table in my bathroom. The table belonged to my Aunt Lucy. At some point during one of my many moves, I painted it an antique greenish-gold and covered it with a white doily my mother had embroidered as part of her wedding linens. I consider all three items to be part of my personal icon collection, and they lend a comfortable, warm and homey energy to the room.

Then there is Ganesha number three, a small carved stone statue that lives on top of the tall cabinet in the foyer next to my front door. It's where I stash my mail, keys, coupons, a few small travel souvenirs, and other miscellaneous items that need a resting place. He sits almost directly under my big gold om.

In looking back at the definition of iconography, I realized I have icons that connect to or represent each subject listed in the dictionary definition: persons, places, things, historical, religious and spiritual. They serve as important touchstones for connecting me to my life and my worldview.

This ends my trip down iconography lane for now, but I'll continue to explore icons that hold a message for me and find a place in my home for new ones that speak a language I may need to hear.

Practice: Icon Tour

Quality to Embody: Exploration

To "EXPLORE" MEANS TO INVESTIGATE, STUDY, analyze or look into. Exploring new ideas and places is enjoyable and rewarding.

A major avenue of exploration can take place right where you live. When you take time to explore and reassess your personal spaces, you may notice locations in your home where the changes you've been experiencing internally now want to be expressed externally in your environment. Ready to find out? Try an icon tour.

On your tour, you may find objects that are nontraditional or unconventional, and that's okay too. When you are ready, choose either a pen and paper, a device with a keyboard, or a camera.

INSTRUCTIONS

This tour takes you through a three-step process. The steps are:

1. Describe
2. Evaluate
3. Implement

Description – The What

The goal of this first step is to make a list of the items that have meaning for you. Consider your answers to the following questions:

- What form do they take (pictures, objects or some other form)?
- Are there items in every room or just one or two rooms?
- Are your selected items in a special location or haphazardly placed?
- Which ones are related to persons, places or things, historical, religious or spiritual?
- Are there other items outside those categories that have meaning for you?
- When and how did you acquire them?

Evaluation – The Why

In this step, you want to explore the significance of the items on your list and how attached you are to them. Consider your answers to the following questions:

- Why do the items have meaning to you?
- Do guests comment on one or more of them? What do they say?
- How do you feel when you look at or think about them?
- How attached are you to them?

- How would you feel if you woke up one morning and found they were all gone? Remember, as important as your icons may be to you, they are still stuff. (Re-read the chapter on "Stuff" if you need a reminder of what that means.)
- Do they fit your current or desired lifestyle?

Implementation – Skillful Action

Put your list aside for a few days. When you're ready to take the next step, pull it out, and revisit one space at a time. Consider your responses to the following suggestions:

- Be conscious of any changes in meaning or attachment you now feel toward your items.
- Make a list of the things you'd like to move, remove or change.
- Check in with others who share your space. Be sure they are in agreement with your choices and make needed compromises.
- Sit tight with any major decisions for a few days to be sure they still "feel" right.
- Make one change at a time.
- Proceed until you experience a feeling of satisfaction and contentment with your decisions.

You don't have to travel far to find a new way of viewing familiar things through a blissful lens.

FINDING BLISS

Occasionally in life there are those moments
of unutterable fulfillment which cannot be
completely explained by those symbols called
words. Their meanings can only be articu-
lated by the inaudible language of the heart.

— Martin Luther King, Jr.

H ow do you find bliss? On a practical level, bliss can be found in the simplest joys of everyday living, and those joys can be experienced in surprising and unexpected ways.

Bliss experiences are the moments when time, space, mind and the ego disappear, and we are absorbed into the present. It's pretty awesome when it happens, but we won't recognize it until it's over because we (the ego) have completely disappeared into the moment.

The first time I experienced this was during a family vacation in Maine. I was twelve years old. We were hiking with friends on Mount Megunticook. It was my first hike, and it was a steep trail. I don't remember what I was thinking as we went up the mountain, but when we got to the top and looked out over the inspiring landscape, I was in awe and lost all sense of time, space and my twelve-year-old ego. I was completely absorbed in the moment. It took my breath away, and I have never forgotten it.

The second deeply intense experience happened when I was a grown-up, during my needlepoint hobby phase. One night, I was transferring an African textile design to a 12″ x 12″ canvas. This process is time-consuming, and it required concentration because I had to color each tiny mesh square in the same color as the yarn that would eventually cover it. That evening, while focusing intently on the process, I lost all sense of time, space, mind and my grown-up ego. By the time I snapped out of it and realized what had happened, an hour had gone by. The design was complete, and I was amazed.

Bliss can also be understood as joy and contentment, which is different from excitement or happiness, which are fleeting and often depend on external factors. Joy and contentment are internally sourced and longer-lasting. On that level, bliss and I are on speaking terms. I know what brings me joy and contentment. My list is long.

At the number one spot is movement. I have an absolute need to move my body, and I'm thankful every day that I can. That love of physical movement and my bliss moment on Mount Megunticook led to years of hiking and backpacking, which has given way to exercise classes, yoga, walking and dancing.

The need to move and the joy it brings manifests in my life in several ways. My first memories of this feeling were the dance classes I took as a child—tap, ballet and jazz. The recitals were a blast. Once, I was chosen to do a solo dressed as a French street mime in Capri pants, a black and white striped shirt, and a black beret. That was pre-teen awesome!

In college, it was modern dance. After college, as an adult, it was keeping up with the latest popular dance crazes. I'm still dancing. As a sixty-something adult, I ended up in a dance recital where I did a ¾-split and got a standing ovation. I used to teach a seniors exercise class at my local YMCA and, to keep them moving and grooving, I made up and taught two dance routines. One was to a clean version of "Blurred Lines" by Robin Thicke and the other to Fats Domino's, "Whole Lotta Lovin'." (RIP, Fats.)

I will dance anywhere and to any music except heavy metal. At indoor concerts, I chair dance because I literally cannot sit still. Outdoor concerts are the best because I can stand up, snap my fingers, and move to my heart's content. Music commands me to move, and I answer with joy. I am simply not able to be still when there is rhythm. I make up dances at home and, like that famous quote suggests, I "dance like nobody's watching."

I got into yoga as another way to move. Bliss happened a few years into taking classes, when yoga evolved from physical movement to feeling blissful, mentally and emotionally.

I have a clear memory of the exact moment when the shift happened. I was working full-time, dealing with a difficult second marriage, and being a stepmom. It was a lot. I was ready, able and looking to get back into a yoga class after recovering from my emergency hysterectomy. I found a class that fit my schedule and committed to going every week. The shift happened one night after class. It began with my car.

Cars for me are a means for transportation, period. They need to start when I turn the key in the ignition and run without problems until it's time to replace them. For me, having a car problem was an invitation to anxiety and panic. Until a few years ago, car problems brought out all my shadow fears about being abandoned, stranded, rejected and uncared for. I would be beside myself with frustration, fear and anger until the tow truck came to charge the battery or take the car to the mechanic.

I came out of yoga class that night and reached into my bag for my car keys. They weren't there. I looked into the car and saw them in the ignition. I walked back to the class where a few students were still hanging out. One of them offered to drive me to the police station. An officer followed us back and worked his magic with a long metal thingy that unlocked the car. I thanked them, got into my car, started it up, and was halfway out of the parking lot when I realized with a jolt—I didn't panic! I was blown away. This was my first visceral real-life example that yoga had moved me toward bliss beyond physical movement.

Another way I experience bliss is with humor and laughter. Laughter, in my mind, is truly the best medicine with many benefits. Laughter can:

- increase endorphin levels.
- enhance oxygen intake.
- stimulate the heart, lungs, muscles and circulation.
- induce relaxation.
- reduce some symptoms of stress.

Laughing a few times a day helps me deal with the little daily f**k-ups, glitches, snags and stressors. Laughing brings a bit of light into all my five layers, even when one is experiencing an imbalance. Having a sense of humor means I can laugh at, or at least see the humor in, life's absurdities, especially my own.

I love, love, love political satire, so I DVR a full spread of the late-night talk shows to capture the opening comedy routines and any interesting guest interviews. I do it because my bedtime is 10:30ish. This way, by the time I have finished my breakfast the next morning, I've had my share of belly laughs, increased my endorphin levels, and have set a positive outlook for the day.

Another way I experience bliss is through creativity. This was sparked during my teenage years. It happened at a meeting of my church's youth group. I've never forgotten what Reverend Herrick, our minister, told us. He said each one of us has a special talent, and it was our responsibility to learn what that might be, then to share it with the world. Well, better late than never, I guess. It has taken decades to surface in a big way for me.

I've always dabbled with writing and have paper and electronic folders full of tidbits, notes, journal entries, chapters, poems, short stories and even a novel, but I never thought of myself as a writer. To me, a writer was someone who had an agent, a publisher and a prominent place on a bookstore shelf and interviews on television talk shows. I put words on paper and on my computer as a way to explore my thoughts without being interrupted, ignored or being told I was wrong. And as Isaac Asimov, the science fiction writer, once said:

Writing is a way to think with my fingers.

For years, I wrote nonfiction academic papers, speeches and newspaper columns on important issues in the civil rights and women's movements of the '60s and '70s but kept the personal fiction and journal stuff tucked away. Now I blissfully write every day and share what I write any way I can. It keeps me sane.

The last thing I'll mention here is volunteering. I have always found time to volunteer in some way most of my life. Helping others helps me feel peaceful and contented regardless of what issues, small, tough or deep, I may be facing. Now that I'm free-tired, I can do more. A few years ago, I set a goal of getting involved with three volunteer projects but now find I'm doing five and may add more.

My Volunteer List

- Contribute posts for several yoga blogs.
- Record a weekly, hour-long radio program entitled "For Your Health" for the blind and print-challenged (people who have visual, learning, emotional, intellectual or physical disabilities).

- Manage a donor-advised fund in honor of my parents. I set it up to provide financial support to yoga and healthy living programs for the at-risk populations in my community.
- Serve on the development committee for a local arts center whose mission is "to celebrate creativity and inspire appreciation for diverse artistic cultures."
- Manage a free summer camp yoga program for city kids.

Bliss is a place I try to visit often, and sometimes it visits me. On rare occasions, I may even take a mini-vacation there, but it is highly unlikely that I, or any of us, will ever be in this state permanently. Daily life intervenes with tasks for me to do, like paying bills, cooking, cleaning, appointments, work and social engagements. And then there are problems, like health challenges, relationship difficulties, accidents and the blues. However, I know bliss is like the sun—it's always there, even on cloudy days. This keeps me joyfully aware and appreciative when it shines in my life.

Practice: Build Your Bliss Stations
Quality to Embody: Joyfulness

BLISS IS BOTH THE JOURNEY AND the goal. We can encourage a bliss state, but we cannot control its appearance or its experience. This is tricky work and not easy, as it requires us to "release and let go" of our attachments and the desire to be in control.

If you want to find your bliss, it's a good idea to have one or more of what the late Joseph Campbell, a professor of comparative mythology and religion, called "bliss stations." A bliss station can be thought of as a place in which to root yourself.

In his book, *The Power of Myth*, he defines it this way:

> *[Sacred space] is an absolute necessity for anybody today. You must have a room, or a certain hour*

*or so a day, where you don't know what was in
the newspapers that morning, you don't know
who your friends are, you don't know what you
owe anybody, you don't know what anybody owes
to you. This is a place where you can simply experience and bring forth what you are and what
you might be. This is the place of creative incuba-
tion. At first, you may find that nothing happens
there. But if you have a sacred place and use it,
something eventually will happen.*

A bliss station can be a space, a span of time, or an activity that
can ground you, calm you, and help you cope with the ups and
downs of life. In a bliss station, you can spend a few minutes as a
human being instead of a human doing. A bliss station will help
you go with the flow, even when the flow is decidedly not moving
in your direction.

If your path lies along the religious, spiritual or philosophical,
you might find your bliss in:

- prayer
- special rituals
- community service
- scripture reading
- fasting
- meditation
- pilgrimages

Maybe your path is material-world practical, and you find bliss
stations in activities, such as:

- hobbies (like sports, gardening, arts and crafts)
- naps

- a cup of tea and a good book on a rainy day
- great sex
- spending time in nature (walk in the woods, canoe, hike, etc.)
- a long talk with a good friend
- spending time with family (that, of course, depends on the family)
- being on the receiving end of an hour-long massage

Experiencing bliss is enough to affirm it exists. It's up to us to find or recognize activities, practices and experiences that take us out of ourselves and take our breath away.

Here's wishing you many blissful moments!

Final Thoughts

You and your five layers of self-awareness form a unique vibration of universal energy. You are a blend of stardust and energy joined together into a perfect whole. Realizing this is what the process of enlightening up is all about. Here are a few last thoughts to take with you on your journey.

The self-awareness process asks us to:

- gain clear knowledge of our character, feelings, desires, quirks and flaws.
- notice and understand the messages we receive from our body and environment.
- get in touch with our breath and energy, and observe how that affects and is affected by our lifestyle and choices.
- watch the mind and emotions, understand the difference between thoughts and feelings, and find ways to respond rather than react to what life presents.
- wake the witness (intuitive wisdom) and use it to work with the first three layers to accept ourselves without judgment, warts and all.
- find our path of connection to something larger than ourselves.

Your journey will unfold at its own pace, based on your choices, challenges and commitment. Respect your pace. Don't allow anyone to hurry you up or slow you down.

You may need to focus on different layers at different times. For example, your body may need to be more active or need more rest. Your mind may want to read, study or contemplate new ideas, or you may be feeling difficult emotions that need attention. Your witness may be asleep and require attention and focus to help it wake up. Be flexible and stay tuned into what you need.

Take time to check on your attitude, actions, reactions, responses and any changes in perspective to gauge how you are doing.

Expect to meet challenges. They are part of the experience and may slow you down, speed you up, or prevent you from making a mistake. Face them with equanimity. They are signposts, teachers and gifts that will let you know which physical, energetic, mental or spiritual muscles you need to flex, rest, stretch or strengthen.

Keep your focus on how far you've come, not on how far you need to go. For the serious traveler, there is no going back, and every step forward gives you the strength to continue.

Throughout the enlightening up process, you will experience yourself as whole and complete. And when you don't, you will have the tools to get back that feeling of wholeness.

Many of us get caught up in the results of what we're working toward or the way things will be when we finally achieve our goals. The truth is that getting to where you want to be doesn't mean the work that led you there goes away. Achieving your version of enlightening up is not an endpoint. You'll need your self-awareness skills to keep moving forward.

I hope your peek into my journey, and those of my friends, colleagues and students, has helped you with yours.

Peace.

Thank you for reading *Enlighten Up!* If you've enjoyed reading this book, please leave a review on your favorite review site. It helps me reach more readers who may benefit from the information provided herein.

ACKNOWLEDGMENTS

Many threads of energy, effort and encouragement come together to move an idea from thought to reality. I am truly grateful for my teachers, friends, students and colleagues whose collective contributions helped make this book a reality.

Thank you to the sages and ancients who distilled their knowledge and wisdom into the writings we read and rely on for guidance on the path to clarity, contentment and resilience.

A special thank you to Joseph Le Page, my primary teacher. He introduced me to the five layers of self-awareness (koshas) that serve as the foundation for this book. He generously agreed to write the foreword, which I take as a sign that I am learning the lessons and embodying the teachings. Thank you, Joseph.

Maria Mendola Shamas and Sandy Eimers are featured in "Three Shades of Grace." Maria and I taught together in many yoga trainings. Her life story is one that keeps you entranced and amazed at the breadth of experiences one life can hold. I'm pleased that she allowed me to share one of hers. I mentored Sandy through the yoga therapy certification process. The answer she gave to one of her written assignments was such a lovely description of a bliss moment that I asked if I might include it in this book. My thanks and gratitude go out to her for saying yes.

Two people deserve thanks for the inspiration that resulted in "Bitchcraft." Cathi Hanauer's essay collections, *The Bitch in The House* and *The Bitch is Back,* were the inspiration for that chapter. My fellow creative spirit and artist/musician son Fred Rawles gifted me with the title during a dinner conversation. Fred get's another thank you for remembering a fact that had long drained from my memory. He reminded me that I wrote the lyrics featured in "The Sky Is Blue, but Why Are You?"

My thanks and gratitude go to the blogs that have featured my writing. Nina Zolotow, Editor-in-Chief of the Yoga for Healthy Aging blog, took a chance on me as a guest writer in 2015. I'm now a member of the writing team and several of the chapters in *Enlighten Up!* are based on posts I've contributed since then. Thanks also to Jivana Heyman, Accessible Yoga; Patti Hamilton at YogaUOnline; and Jana Long at the Black Yoga Teacher's Alliance.

I first met Stephanie Cordoba in the early 1990s. She was on the yoga mat next to mine at a memorable Integrative Yoga Teacher Training on Cape Cod. We've been friends and colleagues ever since. Her professional editing skills have been invaluable. Stephanie edited *Ogi Bogi, the Elephant Yogi,* my book on yoga for children, and did the development edit for this book. Working with Stephanie opened my eyes to the editing process and taught me how and why editors are important and indispensible to writers. Thank you, Stephanie.

Deepest gratitude goes to those who endorsed this book. I can't thank them enough for making time in their lives to read an early draft and write so many kind and heartfelt words to support this book.

Yvonne Espinoza worked with me to design my website, get my Enlighten Up! blog started, and send my newsletters out on a regular schedule. For her technical wizardry, I am grateful. Thank you, Yvonne.

This book would have remained on my computer if not for the publishing expertise of Emerald Lake Books and the work of Tara Alemany and Mark Gerber. Tara's editing, marketing and promotional guidance and expertise took my understanding of the process to new levels. Mark's art direction and understanding of color, design and formatting resulted in a finished product that will give readers a feeling of energy along with the grounding that the book is intended to evoke. Thank you both.

Most of all, thank you to my readers. I hope this book is helpful to all of you on your journey to self-awareness.

ABOUT THE AUTHOR

B eth Gibbs has over twenty years of experience teaching and mentoring hundreds of yoga students, teachers and therapists from all over the world to implement the five-layer model of self-awareness in their professional work and personal practice.

She holds a master's degree in yoga therapy and mind/body health from  Lesley University and is certified as a yoga therapist through the International Association of Yoga Therapists. Beth is a member of the faculty at the Kripalu School of Integrative Yoga Therapy and is guest faculty at The Graduate Institute.

Beth established The Garnett Gibbs Family Fund at the Hartford Foundation for Public Giving in memory of her parents. The purpose of the fund is to support yoga and other healthy living programs in the greater Hartford, CT, region for at-risk populations and people of all ages, especially programs for children in public schools and community settings.

Her published writing includes newsletters, magazine and blog articles on the benefits of yoga, mindfulness and self-awareness.

BETH'S OTHER PRODUCTS

Ogi Bogi, the Elephant Yogi

SCIENCE SHOWS THAT A RELAXED STATE of awareness is optimal for receptivity, learning and problem-solving. In *Ogi Bogi, the Elephant Yogi: Stories about Yoga for Children,* readers will find a collection of original stories that teach children how to attain this state of awareness and use it to deal with issues like self-confidence, social skills, emotions, peer pressure and academic success. It's available on Amazon, BookBaby and Beth's website.

Release, Relax and Let Go MP3

RELEASE, RELAX AND LET GO IS a guided relaxation recording. It is designed to help you increase feelings of well-being, experience positive changes in sleep patterns, enhance creativity, and manage stress levels. It works with your body, breath and mind to bring about a relaxed state of awareness.

The first track gives background information and instructions. The remaining three tracks are fifteen, twenty and thirty minutes in length.

Listen to the first two tracks for free at bethgibbs.com/yoganidra. The full recording is available for purchase on Amazon.

Contact Beth

CHECK OUT THE FEATURES ON BETH's website, bethgibbs.com, read her blog, and sign up for her newsletter.

If you need a speaker or workshop facilitator, contact Beth at emeraldlakebooks.com/gibbs.

For more great books, please visit us at
emeraldlakebooks.com.

EMERALD LAKE
BOOKS
Sherman, Connecticut

Made in United States
Orlando, FL
24 January 2022

13985282R00173